The Subtle Sp

Am I autistic, or is autism something I suffer from? Should I come out, to my friends, to my family, to the people I work with? Should I drop the mask? How can I explain my experience to a neurotypical world?

The Subtle Spectrum offers an exploration into the post-diagnostic landscape of autism and the transformative journey of one woman, from her awareness of difference, through acceptance, to an embracing of autistic identity and beyond as she questions the cultural identity of autism.

Joanna's narrative is enriched with insights from a range of diverse contributors, creating a reflective opportunity for people to gain a better understanding of the experience of being autistic. With a focus on relationships built across a neurodiverse divide, the book considers topics as broad as mental health, work opportunities and abuse, weaving theory and research with lived experience to give true insight into the life of an autistic person, both pre- and post-diagnosis.

Written with a raw and engaging honesty, this is a crucial read for anybody who identifies as autistic as an adult or teenager, or anyone looking to support somebody exploring diagnosis. It will also provide an invaluable insight for social workers, educators and relationships counsellors working with autistic people.

Joanna Grace is the founder of The Sensory Projects and works as a sensory engagement and inclusion specialist. She has been a special school teacher, a foster carer and a support worker for people with disabilities and neurological differences. She grew up on a boat at sea and now lives in rural Cornwall close to the ocean that she loves. Joanna is autistic.

A foreword:

"This wise and compassionate book provides a roadmap toward what author Jo Grace wonderfully calls 'a small private place, unseen by the outside world, a hidden gem' – to personal acceptance of oneself as autistic, and the discovery of autistic community, in a world built for non-autistic people. It's engaging and uplifting reading for anyone on the spectrum, and for readers who want to comprehend the nature of autistic experience."

Steve Silberman, author of *NeuroTribes: The Legacy of Autism and the Future of Neurodiversity*

The Subtle Spectrum: An Honest Account of Autistic Discovery, Relationships and Identity

Joanna Grace

with a foreword by
Steve Silberman

Routledge
Taylor & Francis Group

LONDON AND NEW YORK

First published 2021
by Routledge
2 Park Square, Milton Park, Abingdon, Oxon OX14 4RN

and by Routledge
605 Third Avenue, New York, NY 10158

Routledge is an imprint of the Taylor & Francis Group, an informa business

British Library Cataloguing-in-Publication Data
A catalogue record for this book is available from the British Library

Library of Congress Cataloging-in-Publication Data
Names: Grace, Joanna, author.
Title: The subtle spectrum: an honest account of autistic discovery, relationships and identity / Joanna Grace.
Description: Abingdon, Oxon; New York, NY: Routledge, 2021. | Includes bibliographical references and index.
Identifiers: LCCN 2020053679 (print) | LCCN 2020053680 (ebook) | ISBN 9780367709228 (hardback) | ISBN 9780367709235 (paperback) | ISBN 9781003148524 (ebook)
Subjects: LCSH: Autistic people–Life skills guides. | Autism.
Classification: LCC RC553.A88 G723 2021 (print) | LCC RC553.A88 (ebook) | DDC 616.85/882–dc23
LC record available at https://lccn.loc.gov/2020053679
LC ebook record available at https://lccn.loc.gov/2020053680

ISBN: 978-0-367-70922-8 (hbk)
ISBN: 978-0-367-70923-5 (pbk)
ISBN: 978-1-003-14852-4 (ebk)

Typeset in Verdana
by Newgen Publishing UK

To David and Grace for your candour and kindness, in the hope that identities like ours will be easier to claim in the future.

And to all the people who have contributed their insight and expertise to these pages. Your wisdom and perspective make this a richer text than I could possibly have created alone.

Extra thanks to Jules, Emily, Katie and Clare for reading the first draft and to my husband for managing to live with me as I wrestled the manuscript into shape.

Contents

Contents

Boxes

Preface

How can I possibly write and tell you about my mind? It is like asking a mirror to look into itself. Minds are used for looking out, no mind can really see itself: the belief that it can is akin to the belief of a dog that thinks it can catch its own tail. I know there are places where I cannot see myself. Why would I even try and write a book about things I cannot articulate in life?

Last night I stared at a couple of dozen centimetres of skirting board. The skirting board in question is opposite the chair I sit in to watch television in the evenings. Until a few days ago, the view of it was covered by some red gloves, used to open and close the metal handle on the wood burning stove, and the edge of a cloth laid under the basket of logs which are there to feed the stove. But now it is there. I can see it; this piece of space.

The difference is enormous.

It is the difference between the last few pressurised strokes of a long underwater swim and the easy breathing that comes after the gasping for breath at the surface. Under water I focus, I pull hard, determined that I will make it. Above water my mind is free, I breathe without noticing my breath and I look around at the world.

The landscape of my life changes like this all the time.

How could I explain what that glimpse of skirting board means? Surely I would sound like I had lost my mind.

Is it in some way lost? Lost to me at least? These parts of it I cannot see? Not secret parts, hidden from everyone, but parts hidden only from me. Rendering me all the more vulnerable. Parts that other people see and have a hold of, but that I do not even know are there.

How can I write to you about stuff I cannot see? And yet here in these pages is my attempt to do just that. Chasing my tail around and around, convinced I will capture something with my words. What will you see in this mirror of me?

Identity-first language

Identity-first language is used in this book out of respect for, and in solidarity with, the autistic community who prefer it.[1–12]

Trigger warnings

Trigger warnings are a key part of autistic etiquette. There are many experiences within this book that could be triggering for people but it is not possible for me to anticipate each reader's experience. I can, however, provide warnings for the following commonly triggering topics:

Self-harm is mentioned in chapters: 9.2, 12.3.2, 13.4, and in pop out boxes 15, 17 and 33.
Suicide is mentioned in chapters: 12.3.3, 13.3, 13.4, 13.5 and in pop out boxes 24, 26, 27 and 34.
Sexual abuse is mentioned in pop out box 25.
Bullying is mentioned in 4.5, 4.6, 10.4, 12.3.5 and in pop out boxes 11, 14, 21, 23 and 24.
Domestic abuse is mentioned in pop out box 23.

You will see the letters *TW* at the head of each of these chapter sections or boxes as a reminder that their content may be triggering.

1   Introduction

When writers create books, they have their readers in mind.

Who could these people be?

A good book will be written for well-imagined readers, a bad book will talk only to the writer, leaving the reader to peer in from the outside. I have worried about which this book will turn out to be.

As I wrote this book, I imagined you.

I imagined you as an adult recently identified as autistic. I thought about the shockwaves about to ripple through your life, and the new perspectives and understandings, disappointments and reassurances that these shockwaves could bring.

I imagined you as someone who supports an autistic person or autistic people. I thought of your dedication to that person or people as you endeavour to peer inside parts of the spectrum not previously articulated.

I imagined you as the teenager I once was, but with one key difference: you know you are autistic. I thought of how this knowledge of self might alter your pathway to adulthood.

Whoever you actually are, I am delighted you have picked up this book with a curious mind and I very much hope you find something useful inside its pages.

Many 'me's wrote this book, the me I am today as I go back through the pages with an editorial pen in hand, the me I was six months ago when I began writing, the me I was four years ago when I began researching, the me I was six years ago posting anonymously into the ether of the internet. Our voices overlap each other within its pages.

1

When I first set out to write this book, I imagined I might be able to neatly order the shockwaves and realisations that I, and others, have experienced after we came to know we were autistic into a neat map. I imagined this map to be similar to the stages of grief outlined for people who have experienced a bereavement, or the steps to recovery detailed for those who are confronting addiction. I imagined I understood them as I had been observing them ripple through my own life for a number of years, and I have connected with a great multitude of friends online who all report a similar set of ripples pulsing through their lives.

Surrounding me at my desk as I wrote this book have been piles of notes, some on scraps of paper or lumped together in notebooks, great long lists on continuous streams of computer paper. Still more notes have existed in various locations on my computer, in files and online. There are even diagrams and at times the notes and post-it notes have crept up the walls around me. The ripples are apparent in all of them. I can see them. I can name them: relationships re-evaluated; capabilities and incapacities revealed and understood; decisions taken about whether to 'come out' or not to friends, family members, at work and so on. And yet...

As I have written I have not managed to pull these common themes together into the coherence I imagined. I have worried that using my own experiences as material could come across as an indulgent act of navel gazing, and that I would, in your eyes, fall on the wrong side of the distinction between good book and bad that I drew at the top of this chapter. I have been forced to conclude that whilst there is certainly common ground, the experience of that common ground is *always* individual.

I have failed in my attempts to construct the neat guide I set out to present to you. But I hope that what you have in your hands is all the more human for its imperfectness. In being so I trust it will be easier to relate to than the voice of a know-it-all who *had* managed to map out this territory.

2 Mapping experiences of being a diagnosed autistic: more of a doodle than an Ordnance Survey Map

I set out to map the landscape I encountered as someone diagnosed as autistic in adulthood. What I present to you is more a pen and ink doodle on the back of a napkin than a 1:50,000 OS map. Nevertheless, and in no particular order here are some outlines of what I believe to be common ground.

2.1 Relief

You may have persistently tried and failed to do certain things through the years, things other people seem able to do with ease. You feel relief upon discovering a reason, beyond a lack of effort, for your inability to master these tasks. Akin to the relief felt by a person constantly told off for not listening properly upon discovering they have a hearing impairment.

This may in time be tempered by a growing awareness that certain talents you have prided yourself upon also fall into this new category of 'autistic traits'.

2.2 Questioning how to phrase your identification

Working out how to tell people you are autistic is like trying on items of clothing to see which suit you. Will you say: "I am autistic", or "I have Asperger's"? Might you say, "I suffer with autism", or "I have been diagnosed as autistic"? Perhaps you will prefer "I am on the autistic spectrum", or what about, "I have ASD (autistic spectrum disorder)" or "ASC (autistic spectrum condition)"? You may reach for new terms: "I am neurodivergent" or invent euphemisms: "quirky", "a little out of sync", "different".

In the first instance, it is likely that you will use the phrasing you have heard most often in your life. However, in time you will realise that each of these different phrasings contains within it a set of implications and beliefs about autism. You will come to question the precise meaning of the phrase you first heard and begin hunting for the one that suits you. To go back to the analogy of trying on clothes, you are a child first dressed in clothes by their parents who then begins to dress themselves, and eventually develops a style of their own.

2.3 Deciding who to tell

Once you have worked out how to say you are autistic, or more likely whilst you are still working out a phrasing that suits, you will begin to consider who to tell.

Will you keep it entirely to yourself? Will you tell your family, your friends? Will you tell the people you work for? Would you put 'autistic' on a job application? What about people you meet in passing? New acquaintances, strangers on trains, the person sat next to you on the bus or in the waiting room, the taxi driver? What about professionals you come into contact with: your solicitor, your doctor, your hairdresser, the person who serves you at the supermarket?

Will you tell the world at large? And if so, how will you do it: by wearing a symbol that those in the know could identify? By spelling it out in bold type across a statement t-shirt? Will you write about it anonymously online, or publicly so that anyone who took the time to search the net could learn this fact about you?

Your experience of disclosing this information about yourself, to the first few people that you tell, is likely to shape your attitude towards telling people in the future. Your choices about who to tell will constantly update themselves in light of other people's reactions to you.

People you have told might start to tell other people. How will you feel about other people giving out this information on your behalf? Of course, not everyone will want to disclose that they are autistic as so clearly articulated by Noleta below.

1

Noleta, 15 years old: my diagnosis is my dark secret*

I received my diagnosis at the age of four, but I never knew about it until I was ten years old. When I found out, I froze to the spot. Although I kept an expression of strained joy on my face, my mind was racing with thoughts. At my small village school, people with special needs or learning difficulties were rare. The few there that did need extra help were completely overlooked by their peers. People often used those students' names almost as an insult for being stupid, dumb or acting in a way that the rest simply didn't.

To be identified as different was the worst thing that could happen. As I nodded my head along to my parents' words, fear grew inside me; anticipating what my life would be like should anyone discover my dark secret. To this day at the age of 15, I have only let my diagnosis slip to one person (thankfully they are a close friend of mine). I am utterly terrified at the thought of what might happen, should anyone find out.

> **Surely, you're asking, surely, I've grown to accept my diagnosis and learned to love myself? Throughout these past five years, my views on ASD have never changed – perhaps you could say they have become worse, darker. No matter how many people tell me that I'm perfect as I am or that ASD doesn't define me, I doubt my opinion will ever be altered. My fear is being seen as incapable and that society will judge me based on that.**
>
> **The term Autistic is used as an insult, to mock people, why would I want to identify with that when the word carries so much negativity? You can't change the opinions of others, and acceptance just isn't out there. I want to avoid the label because I desire a full life, with marriage and a good job and all of the things that other people have, without having to prove that I am not less than everyone else. I want people to know me, not a diagnosis.**
>
> * **The people icon indicates that the box is someone's personal testimony/perspective/insight.**

2.4 Thinking about everything over and over again

You may end up thinking everything twice as you ask yourself, "Do I think that, or is autism making me think that?" "Is that me, or is that an autistic trait?" or "What would I think about this if I were not autistic?"

For some people this will be a case of meta-metacognition as you will already have been aware that other people think differently to you and have been wondering, "What would someone else who was not me think about this?" Adding in an identification of autism imposes another layer on this thought and you end up thinking, "What would someone else think, and what would I think if I was not autistic?"

Thinking everything multiple times over can be very tiring. People around you who become aware of your autism may start to do it too, questioning whether your opinions, likes, dislikes, needs and interests are indeed yours at all or whether they belong instead to autism.

The more you ask these questions, the more you will struggle to distinguish yourself from autism. You may feel as though your sense of self is fading as your understanding of autism sharpens. Are you You? Or is the You that you thought you were simply autism?

2.5 Have you been being You or have you been being your best impression of Normal?

A realisation that so much of what you have learned to say and do over the years has been said and done in order to appear neurotypical can lead you to contemplate who you are behind your mask of normality. Many autistics I spoke to in the writing of this book described the process of trying to find themselves, and understand who they really are, as being similar to having a second adolescence. To attempt this process during adolescence itself is undoubtably to brace oneself against the mightiest of teenage experiences.

2.6 Paradigms, prejudices and neuro-normative narratives

As you begin to see yourself as autistic, or see autism as something that relates to your life, you are likely to become increasingly aware of the paradigms, prejudices and neuro-normative narratives in society that make life slightly harder for you. Some people find these as debilitating as living on the top floor of a block of flats that does not have a working lift would be for a wheelchair user. Others experience them as frustrations, akin to being a left-handed person looking for a pair of scissors in a right-handed world.

These barriers fall into two categories: physical and social:

Physical: There are simple physical adjustments that could be made to your environment that would make living within it simpler for you.

Social: There are established social and cultural norms that effect how easy it is to be you.

For example: imagine a world where eye contact was not expected, where public spaces were calm and muted, not loud and cluttered. Imagine a world where everyone took the rules seriously, and where having a passion was respected not pathologised.

As you spot these barriers one by one, you may begin to wonder what an autistic model of life would look like.

You will find inside your own head neurotypical narratives you have been taught, about love and friendship and other topics such as the possibility of a work–life balance, or relaxation, and begin to wonder what an autistic version of these narratives might be.

A parallel can be drawn with the narratives that women grow up hearing: that princesses are beautiful and passive and wait for princes to rescue them. The subliminal teaching of these narratives is that girls are not agents of their own destiny. Who do young girls grow up to be when they are brought up on narratives in which the princess rescues the prince, or rescues herself? Who would autistics be if we grew up in a world where autistic narratives were as valid as neurotypical ones?

2

Part 1: Jeremey: I think I am autistic but I do not want to be diagnosed

I would probably say that I am autistic. I'm not sure how it makes me feel to 'admit' that, but it seems even an odd concept of feeling like it is an admission, as if it is a bad thing. For me it is actually a relief, being able

to understand myself more and how I can maybe deal with situations. It has its frustrations and upsets but it also has its positive aspects.

I remember growing up and mixing in social groups, it was agony at times but I enjoyed feeling part of something. The pain is mental but also physical, I would end up with a stomach ache by the end of it, and this still happens now. The longer the contact the worse it would be. The more familiar I am with the person (and them with me) the easier it is.

Even being in a group of my family (non-immediate, like cousins, etc.) can cause me this social anxiety. I can analyse myself and self-reflect as much as I like but I can't undo this characteristic. I am getting a stomach ache trying to put myself back into a memory to think about what causes it.

If I am out with a small group of people, I will be thinking about what to say, trying to work out when to come in, what tone to say something in and the cadence of it, what might they say back, what might I reply with ... all these things bouncing in my head. It is like being on the starting line of a race and waiting for the gun but for the entire length of the experience.

I know I sound like I am some kind of robot, unaware of how to 'act' normal, like I would be really awkward to be around, but years of experience have made me pretty fluent in Human. I don't think I would generally be detectable. However, if I have too many inputs then it all breaks down, or something breaks.

I find social contact easier when I have a particular role to play. I am a secondary teacher. I am popular with the majority of my students. I get on well with all the staff and I chair the staff committee to organise social events and fun things to help build a sense of community. I wear my teacher self well and I enjoy being in that environment as I don't have to think very hard.

Jeremey the teacher is an easy one; the interactions and conversations are predictable and comfortingly so. In a social situation when I have to be Jeremey the ... person, it becomes much more challenging as I am being judged on myself. The conversations are less predictable and I feel a pressure to entertain, to join in, to go with a flow I cannot always anticipate.

Memories of failed social experiences stick with me. For me it is like they just happened a few seconds ago, I re-live them and feel them and I often come back to them. I've been told that this is common with people who experience trauma, and that description seems to fit. I can immediately be back at a party when I was 17, sitting around in a circle and I had worked out something to say, there was a gap and I had said my thing ... someone then said, "Oh Jeremey, I didn't even know you were here". I remember talking to my Dad in the car saying that these other kids just seem to talk about nothing but could always think of things to say and I could never figure out what to say to them.

I was a very quiet child growing up. I eventually learned how to make decent conversations. Even now, though, I run through possible conversations, possible replies. One of the most common ones being me explaining that I think through all these conversations, even this one (which is a very circular train of thought).

2

Part 2: What would be the use in coming out again?

My reluctance to seek diagnosis is twofold: firstly that I worry that I could be forced to reveal my diagnosis and how this might impact my career or other aspect of my life; secondly I see little benefit from it other than being able to definitively tell my partner that this is my diagnosis, it is real and please listen to me when I beg you for your understanding with this.

In writing that, I'm almost persuading myself to get diagnosed, I can see it would help my relationship. As for coming 'out' as autistic and the way society would view me, well I am gay and I have had to cope with that and I think that is enough for me to deal with. I know from this personal experience of coming out in terms of sexuality, that it is not an out/in situation.

If what you are is visible (skin colour, visible disability), then coming out is not necessary, but if it is internal, then coming out is an ongoing process that happens in every new situation. Even now I will be careful of my use of pronouns with people I don't know as I don't really want to have to deal with that issue if it is not important or relevant.

I have become more comfortable with my sexuality such that I don't care about people's opinions about it and I could deal with negativity, much the same way that I'm sure that I could cope with a neurodivergent diagnosis. I suppose the difference being that I don't need any special treatment from anyone in terms of my sexuality, in fact I don't want any at all, but if people knew about my autism then it may make interactions easier and allow people to understand me more.

The path of progression that Joanna describes finishes with the proud declaration, "I am autistic". It is not one that everyone will travel along. An overused cliché would be that everyone has their own path to travel, but also everyone has their own modes of transport along that path and their own ending.

The assumption made that I would eventually want a diagnosis and to come out is not, for me, a new experience. I have met many people who proudly say that they knew they were gay, then came out to everyone and it was all sunshine and rainbows. They then believe that it should be this way for everyone. Their idea is that if I had the same label as them, then my experience of holding that label would be the same as theirs. This is just a human trait, we understand others through our own experiences.

I did not have a happy experience coming out. My brother threatened to throw a pan of boiling water over me if I didn't leave the house, then eventually my parents asked me to leave so I was homeless for a while. My lived experience helps me to understand others who have had a difficult time coming out, but I can also see that some have had an easier path. I have experienced gay men who get quite annoyed and frustrated by other people's reluctance to come out as gay, or [by the fact] that they are not more 'out' and obvious with it. People compare labels and assume a lived experience, I understand where it comes from and I don't resent the point of view. I hope [that] by sharing my experience I provide balance.

2.7 Wrestling with your own biases, prejudices and stereotypes

In recognising societal biases towards autism, you may come to the uncomfortable realisation that not *all* of these biases exist outside of yourself: some of them exist within you too.

Recognising your own prejudices and stereotypes about autism can be particularly uncomfortable and a certain amount of wrestling with yourself will occur as you try to unpick these from your thinking. A parallel to consider would be that of a homosexual person growing up in a religious community that considered homosexuality a sin. They may come to the realisation that they themselves are homosexual. They may spot society's biases against homosexuality. They may even 'out' themselves as homosexual, declaring their sexuality publicly. Yet in spite of all these things, they may find dark corners of their mind still thinking that homosexuality is sinful, that their sexuality is a defect, and they may experience times when they wish that they were not homosexual. As you wrestle with these difficult topics you may find yourself wishing that you were not autistic.

One of the strongest narratives that surrounds autism is that of it being a disability. Autism is identified through a process of diagnosis which automatically suggests a negative. You do not generally get diagnosed with positive things. Most of us come to identify ourselves as autistic through a medicalised procedure, involving a referral from a doctor to a specialist and so on.

You may ask yourself whether you are disabled and debate within yourself whether autism is a disability, considering social and medical models of disability as you do so. It is likely that you will be challenged by some people who hold up examples of people who occupy a different part of the spectrum to yourself and argue that because you are not like them you are not autistic. Do you have to be disabled to qualify as autistic?

There is no question that some people experience disability through being autistic and lead greatly challenged lives. But we can also point to autistic people for whom the natural abilities of their brains have led them to make incredible contributions to science and technology (or indeed to art or any other discipline).

It seems reasonable to presume that most autistic people fall somewhere between the two extremes, of disability and extraordinary ability, and that the falling between those two extremes is not done in a linear fashion. You may have a person who is extremely able in one situation, but when placed into another situation is disabled by it. As is often pointed out, the spectrum is not a linear spectrum, it is more akin to a colour wheel.

What if being neurotypical was also a diagnosable thing? Would we then recognise that there are extremes to the neurotypical spectrum? Some neurotypical people possess such extraordinary social skills that they are able to use these to climb to spectacular heights in business, industry or the arts. Other neurotypical people are so dependent on their social networks for their emotional stability and wellbeing that they crumble when these needs are not met.

If there were a neurotypical spectrum disorder or condition, would people with autistic spectrum disorder/condition be automatically presumed to be disabled?

Thoughts like this tend to be rabbit holes down which to run. You may find that your mind begins to latch onto one set of questions, insisting that your acceptance of your own autism be determined by the answer to those questions. To draw insight from other communities again, we could consider parallels between the beliefs that people are born gay, or that to be gay is a lifestyle choice. Within the LGBTQ+ community you will find people whose acceptance of their own homosexuality is based on a belief that they were born gay, but you can also still find people who accept their own homosexuality but believe it to be a lifestyle choice they have made.

Going down the disabled–not disabled rabbit hole leads to questions about ableism – and so the internal wrestling continues...

This is the end of my particular list of areas of common ground I have noticed in the post-identification landscape of being autistic. It is by no means an exhaustive list. I fully expect others to come along and add landmarks and features to this doodled map which I would recognise immediately and kick myself for not having noted here. You may also be able to point out flaws in my outlined features that result from my personal view of them; that tower on the hill may appear bigger to me because I am closer to it, it may look different to you because the light falls on it differently from where you stand. As I said at the top, this is a back of a napkin scribble not an OS map. It is a work in progress and I heartily invite you to fill in the bits I have missed and amend any mistakes I have made.

3

Physical differences and research bias*

Researchers have found many physical differences between autistic people and neurotypical people. These include:

- Autistics having heavier or bigger brains[13-15]
- Autistic brains having more neurons, or connectivity differences[14,16-18]
- Autistic brains demonstrating different processing capacities[19-20]
- Autistic brains displaying differences in grey and white matter[21-24]
- The neurotransmitter GABA (gamma aminobutyric acid), which in neurotypical brains acts as an inhibitor dampening visual experience, having no effect in autistic brains.[18]
- Differing levels of hormones such as vasopressin, oxytocin, cortisol, and melatonin between autistics and neurotypicals.[25-31]

In general, the impact of discovered differences is speculated on; for example, researchers[32] found that the brains of autistic children produced 42% more activity when at rest than their neurotypical peers. They suggested that this could lead to a "more pronounced inner life" (n.p.) and account for the impression of autistics as being lost in their own worlds.

Another example of interesting speculation between research findings and lived experience comes from the research into autistic experiences of sleep. Researchers[29,31] found that autistics get less sleep than neurotypicals, and have lower levels of melatonin and reduced periods of REM sleep. REM sleep is thought to play a role in socioemotional regulation. Researchers[30] found autistic people to have significantly different melatonin levels throughout the day when compared to neurotypical people. A spike in the level of melatonin in one's system triggers the 'going to sleep' process. Many autistics report that it takes them an extended period of time to fall asleep; this deficit in melatonin could account for this difference.

It is rare that researchers are able to confidently link their findings to a specific autistic experience. An example[18] of this rare phenomenon is the link between GABA and the experience of visual overload commonly reported by autistics.

In trying to account for differences observed, researchers often seem to find it hard to distinguish correlation from cause. There is an undercurrent of bias in the way findings are reported. For example, Oztan[25] researched hormonal differences between autistic and neurotypical people, and having established them, suggests that targeting vasopressin, a particular hormone, could be a useful therapeutic target. The research was into whether there were differences, not into whether or not the experience of having these differences was a good or bad thing; yet automatically, when a difference is found, the suggestion is to change it in autistic people. The conclusion drawn assumes the differences to be negative. The bias at the heart of much research into autism is further discussed in pop out box 5: 'Genetic differences and research bias'.

One conclusion that rings true with the experience of being on the autistic spectrum is that of Dr Caroline Robertson[18] who reviewed research into neural connectivity patterns in autistic brains for a CNN public lecture. Drawing on insight from Hahamy et al.,[33] she concluded that the best understanding of connectivity in autistic brains would be one of uniqueness. They are not the same as the neurotypical brains, and they are not the same as other autistic brains. This profiling of the autistic experience as unique is one that could be carried across into other areas of autism research as definitive.

* The cog icon indicates that the box is insight from the research community.

3   Travelling from autism awareness to autistic identity

In addition to the common landscape of responses experienced by autistics post-identification, there also appears to be a communality to the journey taken up to, and after, identification. Perhaps because I spend so much of my life on trains, I have tended to think of this journey as a railway line with various destinations along it.

In setting out to write this book, I envisaged that doing so would see me completing the journey and disembarking happily at the final stop. I also felt a strong urge to compel others around me to embark on the journey with me. An urge I now recognise, through the diagnostic lens of autism, as a tendency to think that others think as I think, or ought to think as I think. In recognising this thought pattern, I have been able to evaluate it and temper it with my understanding that each life is different and what is 'right' for one may not be 'right' for another. And in doing all of this I provide an example of the metacognition I spoke about in the previous chapter (section 2.4).

(We could ask whether the tendency to think that others think as we think is an autistic trait at all. Perhaps it is a neurotypical one. More likely, I believe, it is simply a human trait. All humans are prone to thinking that other humans will think as they think. Autistics are pathologised for it, where others are not. In recognising this, we provide ourselves with an example of what I spoke about (section 2.6) with relation to the paradigms, prejudices and neuro-normative narratives that surround our understanding of autism. And in reading this paragraph you have a taster of the sort of exhaustion that can overcome a brain trying to think all of these things simultaneously!)

I no longer think that the end goal is to complete the journey and disembark at the final stop. Instead, I am considering the idea that each person on this journey visits (and revisits) the stations, settling for a time at the stop where they feel most comfortable. The stops are: Difference, Awareness, Understanding, Acceptance, Recognition, and Identity.

3.1 Difference

Before the journey begins, we (autistics) are different. There is, oxymoronically, nothing unusual about being different. What retro-spectively makes our differences noteworthy is that they may have fitted particular patterns; for example, restrictive eating habits, repetitive play, strong interests in particular subjects, sensory sen-sitivities or cravings, social differences, and reactions to affection and physical closeness that do not fit a neurotypical model of normal.

3.2 Awareness

The first station on the line is awareness. In journeying here, we become aware that we are different to our neurotypical peers. Some people feel their weirdness, strangeness, otherness to their peers from their first encounters with their peers. (It is usually peers rather than family members as there is a good chance you will have this particular difference in common with members of your family.) Other people do not notice their difference until they are older. Some do not notice at all and have it pointed out to them by others.

Awareness is like a city that has two stations; the first stop in this double station town would simply be awareness of difference. The second stop, just fractionally further down the track, is an awareness that your difference is of a particular type: autism.

4

My father: I am not autistic

In my opinion, my father and my paternal grand-mother are both autistic , and it is likely that an aunt on my mother's side of the family is also autistic. From conversations with my father, it is clear that our understanding of autism and autistic identity has a generational divide. Here is what he says about autism in relation to himself:

I am not autistic. I agree that I have some autistic traits. I understand that the idea of everyone being on the spectrum is incorrect, but how can I tell if I am neurotypical or not?

I do not feel disabled but accept that I have chosen or followed a life path that is comfortable for me. I do not like the idea of teamwork and lack the confidence others would expect of me. On the other hand, I am able to empathise well, I think. I can get exasperated by frequent plan changes but generally cope well in practical situations, though looking forward to uncertainty can make me anxious.

Autistic used to be used to describe severe cases, but I know now it relates to a range of conditions. I would be interested to know if I am non-neurotypical but it seems by the modern way of thinking only a brain scan can tell. I do not mind what label I am given. I just do not agree I have a disability but admit my mental makeup is not like that of some of my friends.

To normal people of my generation not involved in these conversations the word autistic is associated with extreme disability. I agree it could simply be a difference in how brains process information but few in the general public appreciate this difference. Role models in the media like Chris Packham and Greta Thunberg are bringing awareness, but there is also a risk of a flawed understanding too, of when people find them relatable to, we get back to that idea of everyone being on the spectrum.

5

Genetic differences and research bias

The genetics of autism have been widely investigated. Folstein and Rutter's[34] twin study is cited[35] as being the first clear evidence of a substantial genetic influence on autism. Although there are a few conditions associated with autism that are caused by mutations in a single gene – for example, Fragile X and Rett syndrome – there is no one autism gene.

Geneticists have identified up to 100 genes involved in autism and confirmed that rather than being faulty, these genes are a standard part of our makeup as a population. Silberman[36] (p. 470) summarises:

In recent years, researchers have determined that most cases of autism are not rooted in rare de novo mutations but in very old genes that are shared widely in the general population while being concentrated more in certain families than others.

The concentration of autistic genes in certain families ties in with what other researchers have noticed with regard to autism prevalence rates among certain professions or populations. Temple Grandin and Simon Baron-Cohen[37] both observe a link between engineering and autism. Baron-Cohen et al.[38] found that the fathers and grandfathers of autistic children are twice as likely to be engineers as are the parents of neurotypical children.

The idea of geeks breeding with geeks (assortative mating theory[39]) fuels notions of there being particularly high rates of autism in places like Silicone Valley (which is incidentally also a place highly regarded for its progressive approach to employing people with autism). It is a mould into which I personally fit: both of my parents studied physics at Oxford.

That the genetic differences are not a mutation, but are a functional part of society's genetic structure, makes sense of neurodiversity (see pop out box 29: 'Neurodiversity') as a biological utility: different types of brains are good at different types of things. If autistic brains are particularly good at professions such as engineering then it is no surprise to find more autistics in that field.

We need to tread cautiously, though, as research into autism is riddled with biases and holes. In an ideal world, research would proceed with an open mind, willing to learn and waiting to draw conclusions. Whereas, for example, in the field of genetics, much of the research conducted is funded by organisations hoping to find a cure for autism – if they can identify a genetic mutation, then perhaps they can screen for it: prevent it.

Conclusions such as this one drawn from research which identified that young autistic adults experience a greatly reduced quality of life: "This highlights the fact that ASD is a neurodevelopmental condition with profound effects on quality of life"[245] (p. 903) hint strongly at the presumptions behind them. Consider how it might have been phrased differently if it were another population of young adults being identified as having a reduced quality of life. Would we, for example, state *the fact* that having black skin has profound effects on quality of life? Or would we look for other explanations of the reduced quality of life experienced by people of colour? Following on from such a conclusion, would we expect advice about how to be less black, or advice on how society might change?

Historically, research into autism has excluded certain populations; at one point in time it was defined as a disease of childhood: adults could not be autistic. It has also been considered a male condition: women could not be autistic. Research builds off its foundations, with contemporary researchers seeking insight from the findings of researchers who have gone before them in order to build their understanding of a field. The foundations of research into autism have been laid unevenly so the findings of today's research tend to favour particular groups or positions.

Taken as a whole, research into autism could be viewed as having an obsession with normal, without ever questioning whether normal is necessarily best. Imagine if that happened in another field: if in biology we began with a definition of what a normal plant was and then judged all other plants against that norm, if we sought out treatments for making abnormal plants into normal plants, if we concluded that a plant failing to thrive in a particular environment failed because it was not normal (rather than looking to see if the environment could be adjusted in such a way as to allow the plant to thrive): it would be ludicrous.

In places, the uneven foundations of autism research are being levelled, as autistic-led research organisations – such as the Participatory Autism Research Collective (PARC),[41] the Autism Collaborative Research Cooperative[42] and Academic Autism Spectrum Partnership in Research and Education (AASPIRE)[43] – attempt a paradigm shift, and advocacy organisations such as the Autistic Self Advocacy Network (ASAN)[44] campaign to hold funders to account. The research world's interest in identifying physical and genetic differences involved in being neurodivergent is important; not because it provides a route to preventing such differences, but because it provides a route to understanding and valuing neurodiversity. The application of research focused on developing understanding could genuinely enhance autistic lives, rather than harming them with attempts to normalise their uniqueness. It is hoped that we are heading towards a future where diversity is appreciated not treated.

3.3 Understanding

The second station is understanding. In arriving here, you learn more about autism and increasingly understand how it maps onto your experience of life.

To extend my railway journey analogy probably further than I should, this station is more of a national park or a metropolis than a city. It is an expansive place that fans out in all directions rather than a specific destination/realisation. You may come to understand that your instinct for turn taking in conversations is different to that of your peers and relate this difference to autism. You might understand that the capacity of your brain to focus intently on a topic or a tiny detail is a feature of autism which gives you greater insight into the objects of your focus than your peers have. And so, the list of possible examples continues ad infinitum in a broad sprawling conurbation.

If you are autistic then you are wholly so. There is no part of you or your life in which you are not autistic. Understanding your autistic nature can involve turning every aspect of your life over beneath the lens of autism. Therefore, the understanding represented by this station is as enormous a task as attempting to understand any life in detail would be.

The stations along this journey do not represent tasks to be completed: there is no way anyone finishes understanding their own life, unless they do so from beyond the grave. No one has 'got it' and anyone declaring their understanding complete should be treated with the suspicion that such delusions deserve.

We do not leave this station when our work here is done. Moving on to the next station is more to do with a shift in attitude or desire. The shift can be prompted by a finalisation of understanding particular components of our experience of life, but certainly does not represent us completing the task of understanding.

3.4 Acceptance

I am not sure how far I can sustain my station and place analogy. This stop is a small private place, unseen by the outside world, a hidden gem on our journey. It represents a deeply personal acceptance of yourself as autistic. It is a settling of your understanding and lack of understanding of what autism is and who you are and accepting the two together.

This station shares its name with a term brandished by campaigners looking to change misconceptions about autism in the wider world. They demand that the world at large be more than just aware of autism – that is, know that it is there – and instead accept autism as a part of the rightful landscape of humanity. They want acknowledgement that autism has its place in the world: that it is there and it ought to be so (without a need to be fixed or cured).

There is a distinction to be drawn between the campaign use of this term and what it means to you personally. Both are valid, but only one is on your personal journey.

3.5 Recognising

This station represents noticing the paradigms and narratives that are set against you as an autistic person (as discussed in 2.6). Here you become aware of the inherent prejudice in the world,

6

Autism Acceptance

Autism Acceptance can be seen as an evolution of the pre-existing Autism Awareness campaign.

The film *Rain Man*[45] is often pointed at as the starting point for autism awareness. Up until the success of that film, if you had stopped someone on the street and asked them what autism was, the chances were that they would not have known. Post *Rain Man*, if you stopped that same person, there was a good chance they would say that an autistic person was a savant with poor social skills. *Rain Man* was a great start to awareness, but more was needed. Autism Awareness campaigners wanted people to know that autism existed, that it was a spectrum condition and that not every autistic person was like the character in the film.

Whilst there is still a need for awareness, most Autism Acceptance campaigners would argue that awareness has broadly been achieved and it is time to push for more. Kieran Rose[46] (n.p.) explains:

> 'Awareness' is a passive term, it means you are aware of something, nothing more, with Autism merely that you've heard of a word. Accepting pushes that on, it means listening, learning, understand[ing], empathising, getting off your backside and actually making a difference.
>
> Not everyone can do that of course, but it also means, in a wider sense, accepting that there are many different people in the world who need to do things differently to you. As long as that has no negative impact on you, move out of the way or help. It is as simple as that.

At the time of writing, Autism Acceptance is still a relatively new idea. The Autism Acceptance Project, founded by Estée Klar in 2006 was recognised by the United Nations as one of the first initiatives to support autism acceptance.[47] Klar describes how from 18 months of age, her autistic son's 'beingness' was problematicised by the professionals they encountered.[48] Through her work, Klar continues to ask questions about what we fear in the difference of others and how we might move towards a position where we recognise, accept and embrace that difference.[47]

In the online world, April is Autism Awareness month and the hashtag #AutismAwareness abounds, but more and more now you will see the competing tag #AutismAcceptance cropping up as campaigners push for more than awareness. Paula Durbin-Westby created Autism Acceptance Day in 2011. Durbin-Westby[49] explains that she saw a need for a model of autism "that Autistic people could embrace; something that would not make us feel bad about ourselves, like the 'missing piece,' 'devastating disorder,' and other then-popular and, sadly, still-popular characterizations of autism" (para. 1). Durbin-Westby[49] talks of the harm caused by the autism awareness campaign: "Every April, Autistics and many of our family and friends were swamped with messages about how damaged we were, how lacking, how flawed, how we had no empathy, how we were dangerous, even" (para. 2).

In the late 2000s and early 2010s, there was a feeling among autistics and their allies that awareness raising was no longer desirable, that it was actually causing harm. Durbin-Westby[50] (para. 7) describes the autistic community and its allies as being "sick of impairment- and cure-oriented 'awareness'" Adding that, "It is clear from the way that 'acceptance' caught on with the general public, that the devastating disorder

27

> **rhetoric was not acceptable to many people". Durbin-Westby[50] goes on to explain that "acceptance does not mean 'I accept you, but not your autism.' Acceptance is: pro-neurodiversity, a focus on supports and services tailored to the needs of the Autistic individual, rejection of cure-oriented projects" (para. 7).**

but more uncomfortably within yourself, that speaks of autism as a defect or deficit. You may also recognise yourself as having a responsibility to challenge these paradigms.

The responsibility to do something to challenge prejudice comes about not because you experience it, but because you witness it. You may want to work to change the prejudices you perceive, not because you are autistic, but because you are human and want a fairer world.

3.6 Identity

This station represents the "*I am*" of "I am autistic". The I of identity is a shared I, not an isolated I. It is a community identity. In claiming this I, there is power in the form of self-knowledge. Researchers[51] found that embracing autistic identity was a protective factor with regard to mental health. Here the I is seen not as an isolated, weird, defective thing, but as a part of a wider group. The I is a part of an accepted, understood and recognised whole. This is the identification of self *with* and not *from*, or against, others.

Arriving here signifies coming to a place where you are comfortable owning a group identity alongside an individual identity. Disembarking at this station opens up a previously unseen world of understanding, acceptance, culture and diversity.

I imagine it to be somewhat of a party destination with people celebrating the community they have discovered. I say imagine, because in spite of my best efforts, and in spite of my misguided belief that writing this book would take me there, it is not yet a place I have visited. I have stayed aboard the train and looked out of the windows at the various stations, but I only disembark at the stops I am most familiar with: awareness and understanding.

Fortunately, I have friends who have been to the places I have only seen and they have been kind enough to contribute their insights to these pages.

7

Identity: the masking paradox

Kieran Rose, The Autistic Advocate – adapted from Rose[52]

The act of knowing, starting to unlearn and controlling the Autistic Mask and recognising your Autistic Identity, is a metamorphosis. If you aren't strong enough of mind and heart, it's almost impossible to get through.

But what is the Autistic Identity and why is it so important?

It's a major component of the many aspects that make up who you are.

Your identity as a whole is shaped by your experiences, your race, your education, your skin colour, your sex, your gender, your nationality, your abilities and perceived disabilities.

And it's also shaped by outside influences – it's shaped by judgements made by others and society. Literally how others treat and perceive you plays into its formation.

This Societal conditioning creates expectations of normalcy that, if you don't adhere to [them], creates a conflict with others who are adhering to those expectations. If you are Autistic, the whole concept that everything about you is wrong is being drilled

---

29

into you pretty much from the moment you are born, hence trauma and Autistic Masking to help you conform and hide.

Amongst diagnosed children a really common thing to hear from parents is: "I don't want my child defined by their Autism."

If you are Autistic, one of the biggest drivers of your identity is Autism. It is your neurology and touches every aspect of how you move, communicate, think, feel and perceive the world, impossible to separate from our sensory system. It's all encompassing.

The problem is that if we believe that Autism is only a part of us, it instantly put[s] us at odds with ourselves.

There's always a focus on a part of the person that needs to be overcome, a part which does not exist, so therefore cannot be overcome. It's a paradox.

The result of that is resentment.

A constant war with self that can never be won.

A negative feedback loop that leads to a fracturing of identity.

I know this.

I spent years there, banging my head off of the wall (sometimes literally) over things that I couldn't do – even supposedly simple things like picking up the phone and making a call.

I would ask myself why, get angry and frustrated with myself; hurt myself.

Why?

Because before my diagnosis I believed I was broken.

After my diagnosis there was a reason I was broken.

Nobody ever thought to tell me that I wasn't broken.

That things were just different for me and that was OK; that it's OK that picking up the phone is a herculean task and that if I want to communicate in a different way, it's fine.

Our identity...

Autism colours every aspect of our lives, it is how we perceive the world.

Our Autistic Identity is hidden under a Mask of society's creation.

Society's lack of acceptance forces us to hide in plain sight and, when it identifies us, forces us to accept a narrative about ourselves of its own creation.

The tool for this forced suppression, this oppression, is the language used to pin us down and 'Other' us.

As with anything there are negative aspects to being Autistic, but that doesn't mean that Autism has to be negative.

8

What it means to be part of the autistic community and its culture

James Gordon, trustee of the London Autism Group Charity

In embracing your autistic identity and becoming a part of the autistic community there is a sense of finally being free. Within the community you do not have to hide parts of yourself, instead you are able to converse about them. You can share intimate moments that previously had seemed to be just your own. Suddenly, there is a group of people that have understanding of the same experiences as yourself. There is a sense of belonging like no other.

The autistic community is a place that you can be yourself. Where you can ask questions and find knowledgeable answers from those with genuine lived experiences. Where advice is sought, often about problems many have encountered. It is where different coping mechanisms and methods are shared.

The autistic community has its own rules. When you first become part of it, you become aware of these. The rules mainly centre on respecting each other's feelings. This may mean not mentioning things that are triggering for those around you: many members of the community experience Post Traumatic Stress Disorder as a result of their lived experiences. It can mean not using the puzzle piece symbol that represents a history of oppressive harmful 'therapies' perpetuated by so-called autism organisations that sought to eliminate autism and autistic people.

The community also has a ban on certain language that is trauma triggering, such as saying 'autism parent', 'autism mum', etc. This is seen as the parent stealing the identity of the autistic person, often as a means of putting attention on themselves, in a pity invoking way, while ignoring the difficulties of, and talking over, the autistic person.

By forming groups and self-advocating the autistic community have come together to produce their own cultural events that reflect their shared identity. There are now autistic-led organisations that offer families and individuals support, education and leisure opportunities. There are autistic-led retreats and conferences for discussion by and for autistic people; for example, Autscape. These are centred on the needs and interests of the autistic community.

Autistic culture has a wealth of written and artistic expression. With the advent of the internet, these materials are widely accessible. There are collective libraries of autistic writers and bloggers, such as those compiled by the Flow Observatorium that campaigns for the visibility and understanding of neurodivergent artists. Autistic-led theatre companies such as AutAct produce amazing plays, such as *The Duck*, in which the drama is played out from the perspective of a woman freshly diagnosed in adulthood, written by autistic author Rhi Lloyd-Williams.

Being part of the autistic community means belonging to a group that gives you respect and equity. This can be experienced by attending events organised by autistic-led organisations throughout the year such as Autistic Inclusive meets. Or by attending one of the Autistic Pride gatherings that take place across the summer months. These gatherings allow us to experience our own shared identity, in environments tailored to our mutual sensory and neurodiverse needs, on our own terms.

Knowing that we are not alone, and being able to see many of our neurodivergent peers with our own eyes (which is a rare thing for most of us), can be incredibly uplifting. The experience can be powerful, helping to build confidence and as a result boosting mental health. It gives autistics, [who] have often felt excluded, a chance to participate in a community that we can truly call our own. Within the autistic community the social playing field is levelled. Many of us share or at least understand difficulties in interaction. Thus there is an atmosphere of respectful patience where friendships can be forged and we can finally enjoy the rights that others have always taken for granted.

4   Fragments of difference

This chapter is a collection of childhood memories that point towards autism. These are memories recalled, rather than knowledge reported. I have not been able to research and create them for you; rather, they are found whole in my mind like dreams remembered after a night of sleep. In sifting through my memories, I have tried to pick ones from different times in my life; for example, in the Playgroup example (4.1), I am probably two or three years old, whereas by the time we are in the second playground (4.3), I would be around seven years old.

4.1 Playgroup

I am stunned.

Motionless.

The lady who runs the nursery mentions to my mother that I do not play like the other children do.

I stand rooted to the spot where I am left. At home I play with LEGO®. At nursery, I stand near the giant brightly-coloured plastic building blocks, each one the size of a 4-litre tub of ice cream. I want to play with them, but I do not.

Next to the bricks is a rocking horse, and in the middle of the room a square climbing frame low enough for an adult to reach you down from the top.

I do not know what is on the other side of the room.

I am not afraid, or defiant. I am stuck in the pause before movement. I am here. I am taking stock. Once I have understood it, I will act.

Only I cannot take it all in.

There is too much going on and I have no clues as to what I am supposed to be doing.

4.2 The playground

I am in the playground. My world is a few metres of sunlit grey asphalt. Beyond it, children run and shriek. I squint my eyes and look into the sun. The light splinters through my eyelashes in rainbows. I do this over and over again.

Back in the classroom, I try to draw the splintering light, but my coloured pencils are an inadequate match for the beauty I saw.

I write in my workbook that I want to be an illustrator when I grow up.

4.3 Another playground

I am in a different playground. It is dark, a large block granite wall towers above me. I have not ventured across this playground to the far side where the wall stops and a chain-link fence sections us off from a grass field beyond.

Children passing me shout at me, their eyes fix on me. I feel threatened.

I turn. As I turn, my hands, hung on the end of my arms swing up slightly. I turn back, my hands rise up further. I turn, and turn, and turn. My hands draw an arc around me, first at thigh height, then hip, then waist, sometimes flying at chest height. The faces of the children blur but their shouts remain. They are not shouting at me, but I do not know this. They are shouting about the games they will play, calling out to each other to join in. But I just hear shouts.

I begin *The Jungle Book*. Reciting the words of Rudyard Kipling aloud to myself. I know the two-hour story tape by heart. I repeat it every playtime.

4.4 Shadows

A new playground. Part sun, part shadow. I stand in the corner with the most shadows. I think of myself as hidden.

Once in a while an adult will move me on, saying, "Go and play", "Run around with the others", forcing me into the no man's land of undefined space.

The children in this playground do not notice me as much. I get braver and allow myself to stand on wet patches on the ground, because they are the same colour as the shadows. On playtimes after rain showers, I leap from puddle edge to puddle edge and back to shadow again.

Occasionally I am assailed by peers. I am instructed that I am "It". I am obedient and chase after the blur of red gingham dresses. I am ordered to line up with my back against the wall and learn the lyrics to a pop song. I stand as I am told. The other children know the chorus, our self-appointed teacher knows all the verses. I do not know anything. In the chaos of this improvised classroom with its power-crazed child teacher, it is easy to slide back into the shadows.

I am no trouble to anyone.

4.5 Trees and toilets

TW

In the next playground, the children are older, and there are fewer shadows. Being cast adrift in the space with no clear designation of where to be feels menacing. There is an outdoor toilet block, and a large tree. I experiment with standing behind the tree but am too often disturbed by chase games whipping around its trunk. I lock myself into a toilet cubicle instead, always the third one from the end. I feel safe. No one looks at me here.

But it isn't safe to be strange.

Spending all my time in the toilet earns me a variety of humiliating nick-names.

4.6 Sticks and stones

TW

A teenager now, and I am allowed to walk by myself around the village where I live. My peers hang out in the park, sitting on a low wall, learning to kiss boys and sharing bottles of cheap alcohol.

I walk past, eyes averted, heart thumping. I pretend not to hear them as they call out to me. Wet toilet paper is thrown at me.

I take this to be a sign that they remember me from primary school.

My family are obliged to like me. These people are objective judges and they have spoken. I take their judgement seriously.

5 Reflections on difference

This chapter looks at how I came to notice my particular difference and questions whether a child who was like me, as I was then, would benefit from support and, if they would, how it might be given. It also examines how my remembering of these experiences is in itself different to the expected norm and explores the value of this difference in my life.

5.1 Everyone is different

At home I was not different. At home I was just me: I was well-loved and always busy with some project or other. Running out of Sellotape was the worst thing that ever happened at home.

Home was always, and remains always, a safe place. I have never wanted to sully it with anything from outside. Home was for home. School was for school.

Being different is not unusual. People are different because they are from another school or town, because they wear glasses, or have ginger hair or black skin. People are different because they have a different accent or move in a different way.

I learned I was different slowly, through exposure to my peers. I was different, but it was not clear to me why.

Without anything to ascribe my difference to, I concluded it must be *me*. *I* am different. Lacking alternatives, this understanding of myself as a fundamentally different sort of person became foundational to my identity. I acted to perpetuate it. If everybody else liked something, I chose not to. If a certain item of clothing was in fashion, I would not wear it. Not only was I unaware of who the boy bands at the time were, I actively did not want to know. If I had to be different, then I was damn well going to be different.

5.2 Could things have been different?

At nursery, people could have helped me by making my world smaller, and giving me a clear sequence for what was expected from me. But I do not remember myself in that moment as someone who needed help. No distress was caused by existing in that pause before action.

Time could have been taken to help me become familiar with the toys, screens could have shielded me from having to take in the whole environment at once. In my memory the other children are not there, but of course the room would have been filled with my adventuring peers. Had I been able to take them in, I might have picked up the clues I was missing about what to do. It is likely that on my own, or in a set-up with fewer children, I could have initiated play.

What causes that pause?

Was I understanding more slowly than the other children the lie of the land?

Or, was I taking in everything in greater detail?

Did I have a higher requirement for knowledge before action?

To this day, I will only do something if I feel I have amassed sufficient detail about what that thing entails before doing it. In the way that another person might ask for the dress code before attending a party, I do this to the nth degree. I gather every piece of information I can, including walking routes on Google Maps and looking up photos of rooms so that I know where I am. Once I know where I am and what is expected of me in that place, then I act. Without knowing, I freeze.

You are unlikely to catch me frozen, not because I have grown out of freezing, but because I have grown in my capacity to amass the level of knowledge that I need prior to acting.

In more formal learning environments, it was easier for me to understand what was to be done. Some autistic students benefit from seeing a completed example of the task they are being set before they attempt the task itself. Showing what free-play looks like completed is a difficult thing to do. Adding structure and routines to the free flow of the early years' environments could make them more accessible to a child like me.

In the playgrounds, an adult-led structured play activity could have seen me join in games alongside my peers. Equally I would have been content to engage with my own world, with the shards of sunlight, the tiny animals I noticed, the glints of stuff in the granite, if in doing that I could have been kept safe from bullying. A whole-school understanding and acceptance of difference (as is commonplace in many special schools) would benefit all children.

5.3 Slow-motion memories

Memories from childhood process very slowly through my mind. Is this me being slow? Or is this me being more thorough than the next person?

My life and my memory of my living have not kept pace with each other.

At eight years old, my mind was constantly occupied with memories of my life aged two to five.

At 12 years old, I thought about every social exchange of which I had been a part at primary school: what had it meant when we lined up to get our work marked and the girl ahead of me had commented on my teeth? What should I have said when in the playground I had been asked if I knew what an Ewok was? And so on in an almost endless churn of moments not quite understood at the time.

My mind needs to understand these things before it moves on, and there is a backlog.

A boyfriend from my thirties complained, "You always go on about school"; by that point in my life the background track of my brain had me going through my teenage years.

As I write it still plays, I am 40 plus, but my brain is still processing my early twenties. Perhaps if I sit very still for a long time it will catch up with where I am.

I never skip a bit. I feel a responsibility towards understanding my actions and deciding whether they were right or wrong, whether there would have been a better course than the one I took.

There is a use to this 'no stone unturned' approach to life. We are all affected by our early experiences. If we allow this to happen without attending to it, then we can make no choices about the impact of our experiences upon ourselves. But if we inspect those experiences, we can exercise some control over where they sit in our psyches.

Take the wet toilet paper incident I described in section 4.6 as an example. In my memory that is something that happened often. But memories are untrustworthy. Holding onto an unchecked memory of constant persecution could undermine your self-esteem.

Reflecting on that memory, I expect that it only happened once. I expect I walked past unchallenged most days, merely fearing that they would remember my playground nicknames.

I expect that on the day the wet toilet paper balls hit my neck and face and I took them as evidence that they remembered my playground nicknames, it is equally likely that the toilet paper fight was just the fun they were having that day and nothing to do with me at all, aside from the fact that I happened to be walking past. It seems probable that they had thrown them at each other as much as they threw them at me. I doubt they loaded them with the significance I perceived at the time.

The nicknames from primary school would have been said because they were funny, not because they had sat about as a jury of my peers and decided my worth. My understanding of their words' significance at the time was based on what my own words would have meant then if I had spoken. Most likely they were simply commenting on the odd location where I chose to spend my playtimes.

If I had left those memories unturned, I could have crushed my own self-esteem with all the additional weight I gave to the significance of their actions. I could have resented the people involved.

I still see many of those people now, through the window of social media and in real life as we walk past each other in town. They remember me as a quiet girl they went to school with. They are good people, whose lives I feel privileged to watch unfold. From time to time, we have been able to help each other out. In knowing them and being known there is a connectedness which makes the world feel like a gentler place. I expect, and hope, they have no memory of the small actions that so seared my memory.

Their actions in my memory do not speak of what sort of people they were or are. They say only that they were children, teenagers, learning how to be as everyone learns. I can find just as many memories, if not more, of times when my own behaviour, my silence, my remoteness from shared games, my lack of interest in hot topics of discussion, could have been interpreted by someone else as offensive. Indeed, people have told me that they found me to be "stuck up", "snobbish" or "aloof".

Remembered acts, once so dominant in my thinking, fully inspected, digested, can be allowed to fade in their significance so that my sense of self is built on more rigid foundations. And herein lies the worth, I would argue, in the thought that I give my personal history. But it is an epic task, the presence of history in the present often frustrates those I am close to who would welcome my engagement with the day in hand. And though I might defend this effort of memory as a worthy endeavour, it is not a choice. I cannot switch off this line of thought in my mind.

Given the detail above in this single summarised version of one event, you would be right to question the utility of such comprehensive reflection. Is doing this useful? Or is it a hindrance to the present?

9

Slow-motion emotions

In writing this book, I wondered whether my experience of slow-motion emotional processing was unique to me or a common feature of this particular part of the autistic spectrum. I asked online communities of autistic women. The responses were varied. Some people suggested that what I describe matches better with accounts of emotional trauma, others reported feeling themselves to be emotionally immature, and some reacted to my question with cries of recognition.

Yet even within the cries of recognition – "I can so relate to this!" and "That is exactly me!" – I found expressions of difference. One woman said she tended to be five to seven years behind always; another said that her processing was delayed but only by a matter of weeks; someone else said it felt to her as if her emotions were on hold, she feels nothing in the moment and then years later knows what she felt about a particular event.

One commentator queried whether it was actually my emotional processing that was running in slow motion or whether what I was undertaking was more an act of re-evaluation. They reported themselves as feeling and responding in the moment, or near enough, but years after still wanting to go back and assess what had happened and evaluate their own responses. They reflected that they are able to think of so many things they should have said or done that it is easy for them to feel stuck in the past.

These 'in community' conversations helped me to reflect on my own experience and how it might overlap with other people's experiences of autism. In line with the idea of autism being a spectrum of experience, I feel vindicated in saying that the slow motion of my background emotional track is an aspect of autism experienced by some people on the spectrum. I am also at ease suggesting that the emotional processing of autistic people does not conform to standard models of processing: there may not be any one way of pro-cessing emotions autistically, but to process emotions in a unique or idiosyncratic way seems to be an aut-istic trait. This echoes Robertson's[18] comments on uniqueness being definitive of autistic processing (see pop out boxes 3: 'Physical differences and research bias'; and 5: 'Genetic differences and research bias').

6   Fragments of awareness

As the child standing rooted to the spot at playgroup, or hiding behind the tree at playtime, I was easy to identify as different. As an adult I have blended in more, but I have regularly encountered situations in which I have felt as alien from those around me as I felt as a child in the playground. In this chapter I have collected up a few memories to illustrate this experience of otherness.

6.1 Watching paint dry

My friends and I sit around the dinner table. We have all recently purchased our first homes. DIY is a necessity. They discuss paint. In particular the drying time of paint. Debating which brands dry more quickly. I do not take part. I listen aghast that they are really talking about paint drying. "Watching paint dry" is a reference point for extreme boredom. Surely, they would not talk about something widely recognised as boring, when better topics were available. We could discuss the nature of love, the moral value of particular exchanges in our lives, we could debate the environmental impact of our food choices for the meal. Surely talking about paint drying is a mistake? But they persist.

Eventually I can take it no longer. I slap my hands on the table to interrupt everyone. "Do you realise?" I stress, "that you are talking about watching paint dry?"

Everyone pauses and looks confused. Yes, they realise: they are fully aware of the topic of conversation. What is my point?

6.2 The yoghurt conundrum

I once worked as a teaching assistant in a school. At lunchtimes I sat in the staffroom with the teachers. All of the teachers were specialists in their subject areas, it was a secondary school. They knew a lot about interesting things. They had families, and stories from those families of stresses and successes to tell. They had hobbies and interests, many embracing an adventurous outdoorsy life. But they did not talk about these things.

I did not talk at all. I read biographies and accounts of people climbing mountains or going mad. And I listened to the conversations around me. Everyone always sat in the same place.

The girls opposite me talked about their diets. Had they been 'good' or 'bad' at the weekend. Good did not mean they had helped old ladies to cross the road or picked up other people's dog dirt. Good meant they had not eaten. Bad did not mean they had shouted cruel words at people, or kicked a cat, bad meant they had eaten and enjoyed food. The conversation was the same every week.

To their left, three older teachers sat with a younger member of staff. The potential for that younger member to have learned from the wisdom and experience of the older staff was, for me, palpable. The younger teacher always had a yoghurt for dessert, and at some point prior to my arrival at that school, she had once opened her yoghurt and a small blob of that yoghurt had launched itself from the plastic cup and landed on one of the older teacher's tops. Consequently, every lunch time when she lifted her yoghurt from her packed lunch box, the older teachers made remarks along the lines of "Oh watch out", or warned other members of staff sitting nearby to shield themselves. Every day. Every day the same conversation. The same wasted opportunity to share insight and wisdom.

Think of all the hours of their lives these people will have spent repeating the same words, empty of meaning. Think of what those hours could have been filled with. I spent a small fortune in bookshops and filled my hours with the words of Nelson Mandela and Terry Waite, and Joe Simpson, and Lionel Shriver, and Milan

Kundera and so many more. Whilst they repeated, what to me were the same inanities day in day out.

Last year I happened to attend a lecture where it was explained that social chit chat serves the same purpose for people as grooming does for monkeys. We were shown footage of monkeys grooming each other: sometimes they groom one another because they need grooming, but often the grooming is unneeded and done as an act of bonding. In the act of pulling small bits of dirt and fluff from another's fur there is the expression of "I am here", "I care about you", "I am attending to you". It is in many ways kinder and more poignant when performed to serve no functional purpose. It is done purely to connect with you, regardless of whether you need the service or not, just because you are you.

Small talk, we were told, serves the same purpose as grooming in monkeys.

That information has lodged in my head. Crystal clear. Now it makes sense why all those brilliant people persisted in doing something so apparently illogical and wasteful. But all my other well-reasoned arguments remain. I still do not want to talk about paint drying. And I do not think one small accident with a yoghurt from years ago worthy of replaying daily.

Would I argue that the same connection could be made through worthy discussion? Deep conversations do, after all, bond people. But I imagine people would be exhausted by a requirement to discuss the depths of their soul daily at lunchtime. I can see why they stick to a pre-written script.

Am I wrong?

Are they wrong?

6.3 Scripting conversation

I do not object to pre-scripted conversations. Most of what I say is pre-scripted. My current job is providing training to people who support individuals with profound and multiple learning disabilities. Everything I say during a training day is scripted. Of course, the presentation is, people would expect that. But so are all the tangents I appear to take spontaneously. So are the slip ups

I make to humanise the monologue. So are the questions I ask people when chatting in the breaktimes.

Of all the content I deliver, you might imagine the more technical stuff to be the hardest to remember, but for me the trickiest parts of the working day are arriving and saying hello to people before I take the platform at the front, and the downtime in between lectures. On a great many occasions, I have opted to lock myself in a toilet cubicle rather than tackle these parts of the day where I so readily fail. It is easier to just participate in the bits I am good at.

It is only in the past couple of years that I have developed a script for these 'before and between' parts of the day, and it is still very much a work in progress. I will ask people, "Where are you from?" which works to some extent but often leads to short answers I can do nothing with. Or I will ask them, "What would you usually be doing on a Friday?" which is better as it leads to longer explanations.

The benefit to me of being the trainer in these circumstances is that no one really expects you to spend much time with them, you are expected to talk to everyone. So one question can get me through a good chunk of a 20-minute break and the rest can be filled with going to the toilet. Locking myself into toilet cubicles has remained throughout my life a very practical coping strategy for social situations.

Towards the end of a training day close observers would be able to spot me beginning to chew my words, especially on days where I am at the end of delivering several days of training back to back. I will mangle a word or two in a sentence as I say them. This is the beginning of me exhausting my communication capabilities.

I catch the train home, continuing to communicate near constantly, but not by talking. Online communication, typed, is so much easier. I can re-read my sentences to check they say the right thing. I can decorate them with emoji indicators of what tone they are meant in, rather than trying to find that correct tone with the modulation of my voice. I can even state in writing the tone they are meant in as you cannot generally read tone, so online it is acceptable just to label it.

The train ride is usually over five or six hours. I think of this time as buffering. When I get home, my husband has learned to access whether I can talk or not. Sometimes he will ask me something and my reply will come in slow motion. I do not realise myself that the spaces between my words are too long, but if that happens, he tends to stop talking and just put me on the sofa to watch television. At other times he gets no response. I see him. I see that he is talking. I wait for the talking to get to me, but it is like time has slowed and his words stretch across it and form a noise, not a meaning. I stare at him. I could not be accused of not listening, of not paying attention. I am just blank. Pre-diagnosis, these responses used to get me into a lot of trouble with partners, as understood through a neurotypical lens they are dismissive or careless. Post-diagnosis, it is easier, although not easy.

By the time I get home on a normal week my husband will not have seen me for a few days. He looks forward to my coming home. He must crave a reflection of his own emotions in my expression upon arrival. He would love it if my face lit up at the sight of him, and if I came readily towards him to embrace him and ask him about his time while we had been apart. It is one thing to know that the glassy stare is nothing personal, but it does not remove the impression of disinterest that my blank demeanour must generate.

6.4 Job interview

I mentioned in section 6.3 that locking oneself in the toilets is a practical solution to social challenges. I would add to that a note of caution: it is only practical when used in small doses.

I once landed a job interview for a job I really, really wanted. It was to work in a creative way supporting socially isolated youngsters at a hub that catered for teenagers with neurodivergent conditions and teenagers from chaotic backgrounds. There was loads of scope for making the job into whatever you wanted it to be.

The job description said they wanted someone who could connect to the young people and then engage them in a creative task. With a role, and a position of seniority, like teacher or mentor, I am good at connecting with children and teenagers who seem – to others – to be different. (The communication-enabling nature of having a particular role is something Jeremey also reflects on in pop out box 2 part 1: 'Jeremey: I think I am autistic but I do not want to be diagnosed'.)

My slow processing of my life's emotional legacy works in my favour when I look to relate to teenagers. Although when I was a teenager, I had no understanding of what was going on, the work I have put in as an adult to process my teenage years means I could never be accused of being an adult who is out of touch with how dramatic and vital a teenage life can be. It is more recent in my understanding than it would be for someone who was able to process it at the time. I viscerally remember how important things, that other adults now might dismiss as childish, are when you are living through them.

The job was heavily competed for, hundreds of applications were received and only 12 of us were called to interview. I had heaps of relevant experience; after university I set up and ran my own youth club for teenagers in my locality. Through my life I have in one way or another been involved with supporting people who have learning disabilities or physical disabilities. I had a creative background to reference, an A-level in art and all sorts of weird sticky-tape-based projects along the way that made for colourful curious photos to submit with an application.

I planned for an interview. I wore smart clothes. I practised possible answers to possible questions, over hundreds of possible permutations of what those questions might be. And then the day arrived. The hub is a converted church, the walls inside have been decorated by a graffiti artist and from the main room corridors lead off to studios and sports halls. I walked in and that first room, the room that would have been where the congregation sat, was full of people.

I found a small reception desk, smuggled like a DJ booth into one corner, and said I was there for the interview. The alternatively dressed cheerful receptionist waved me towards the crowd. "Just go and join in", she smiled, "Tony will be doing an announcement shortly".

Tony was the manager of the place. I had, in my extensive research for the interview, looked up the backgrounds of all the leading members of staff on the team so that should they be on the panel interviewing me, I would be able to say things relevant to their interests that demonstrated my own understanding of their skills and the importance of certain strategies.

Just like when the dinner ladies waved me away from the playground shadows at school, telling me to "go and play", I stepped out into the no man's land of that room.

Off to one side someone had an urn and was serving teas and coffees and there were big plates of chocolate digestive biscuits. Lining up to get a tea or coffee was the only structured activity taking place. So even though I was not thirsty and did not want a drink of tea or coffee, I lined up and got a tea. I also collected two chocolate biscuits.

I ate the first biscuit quickly to get the sugar into my bloodstream and feed the need for adrenalin production. I milled about a bit eating the other biscuit and sipping the tea, I tried to perform a big interest in the graffiti, craning my neck upwards away from all the faces in the room. Justifying this to myself as permissible because maybe my watching interviewers would recognise me as someone very motivated by art, who would be good at motivating the teenagers attending the centre to do art.

Finally, Tony banged on a cup with a teaspoon and the room hushed. We were invited to sit on steps or get comfortable in any way we saw fit. He explained that the centre is a community and that everyone is a vital part of its working. Alongside the team of tutors, which I was hoping to join, there were also admin staff, volunteers, fundraisers, cleaners, managers and leaders. He asked each of the 12 candidates to wave and introduce themselves. This we all did in turn. He went on to explain that they already knew each of us was more than qualified to take on the role. He complimented us on the number of people we had beaten in order to be in that room; he said the standard of application overall was terrifically high.

All they wanted to know was how well we would fit in with the team. So, tea and biscuits were to be in constant supply and for the next hour we were invited to chat and have fun meeting everyone. The managers (who were not pointed out to us) would be the people who made the final decision about who got the job, but everyone's opinion counted and the managers would be watching our conversations and asking the people we talked to what they thought of us.

We were to be judged on our ability to navigate a social environment.

I took two more chocolate biscuits and stood in a group that had one other candidate in it and about five members of the team asking questions. This candidate was a sculptor, and his chosen material was slate – which is such an impressive thing to even attempt to sculpt. He was tall and beautiful with dark soft curling hair and had an easy manner to him. He asked me what I did, redirecting the attention he had fairly won generously onto me. I answered with one of my pre-prepared interview question answers, a best fit for the situation. The group listening took this answer in politely and then moved their attention back to him, his affable nature was much easier to be around than my clipped reply.

I fetched more tea.

Looking back out into the room, I saw him with another group; he was working the room, making sure he spoke to everyone. I went over and stood to the side of the group. He had not yet told them he sculpted with slate. That announcement had gone down so well in the first group. I knew it was next on the list of things to be said. Someone turned their attention to me, so I said it: "Did you know he sculpts with slate, that is so impressive isn't it?" Everyone agreed, my words were warmly received. I felt pleased, I had completed the social exchange correctly. But my words were not about me. I was failing the interview. I stood and listened again to his account of the sculptures he made and his heartfelt reasons for wanting to reach out to the children who attended the hub.

Those children would surely be better served by someone warm and personable like him, than by someone clipped and reserved like me.

I collected more biscuits.

I went to the toilet.

I did not leave the cubicle until I heard the summons for everyone to gather together and the interview to end.

Needless to say, I did not get the job, I doubt most of the people there even knew I attended. When the managers went through their list of 12 people asking for the insights gathered, no one would have known anything about me.

In contrast, I have never failed to get a job I have been formally interviewed for.

Was it a fair litmus test? Or was it one biased in favour of neurotypical people?

Was I right that the children would have been better served by his personality than mine?

In other similar roles, I have made deep connections with children. The centre ran a provision for teenagers struggling with their autism. Might I have had more in common, more potential to understand and identify with them, than him?

Had I been diagnosed as autistic when I attended this interview would disclosing that diagnosis have made a difference?

Incidentally, slate sculpting man did not get the job either.

10

College students: we hate our diagnosis

Anonymous

I am a teacher. I used to teach students with profound and multiple learning disabilities, but now I work at a high school for students with autism. Yesterday was Autism Awareness Day, and everyone was wishing people a happy autism day. It sat uncomfortably with my students. They are at the stage where they hate their autism.

I try to promote role models from the autistic community and I stress the individual strengths of my students but they still hate their autism. They are looking at job opportunities and it is overwhelming for them. Role models do help them to envisage themselves as able to make a positive difference to their community, but it is so hard. They are convinced that they will not get a job because they are autistic, and sadly, the statistics support their belief.

11

Employment of autistics

TW

In 2016, The National Autistic Society[53] reported that only 16% of autistic adults were in full-time paid employment, and only 32% of autistic adults had some form of paid work. This contrasts with the Office for National Statistics reports at the same time of employment rates above 74% for the general population[54] (employment rates at the time of writing are over 76%[55]). Researchers globally recognise that autistic people are disproportionately unemployed or underemployed.[53,56,57–60]

There is "ample evidence"[61] (p. 125) of the benefit to employers and companies of hiring autistic people, with employers rating their trustworthiness, reliability, attention to detail and focus. But gaining employment can be difficult for autistic people; Milton[62] highlights the salience of the double empathy problem (see pop out box 19: 'Double empathy research') with regard to the social encounter of the job interview. Experiences of employment are likely to be different for autistic people in comparison with neurotypical people; for example, 48% of the autistic respondents to the National Autistic Society's survey[53] on employment reported having experienced workplace bullying. This stands in stark contrast to the figures associated with the general workforce which put experience of bullying between 23%[63] and 29%.[64] The National Autistic Society survey[53] also drew attention to social and environmental factors that can make the workplace harder for autistic people to thrive in than neurotypical people.

Whilst there are laudable examples of preferential hiring policies in place at high-profile organisations like Microsoft[65] and Ernst & Young,[66] who ask, "Do great minds always think alike?"[67] as they highlight the unique talent autistic people can bring to the workplace, these remain exceptions to the rule.

There are also organisations focused on bringing together employers with neurodiverse employees for the betterment of both parties; for example, the Neurodiversity hub in Australia.[68] Untapped[69] highlight statistics showing better productivity and retention rates amongst a neurodiverse workforce when compared to a neurotypical workforce. Attention has been drawn to the role played by intersectionality in access to these apparently inclusive preferential hiring schemes.[56,70–71] The schemes preferentially seek out characteristics common to autistic men, without recognising the different strength profiles of autistic women. Kirby[72] reports the frustration of autistic women who feel that they have not fulfilled their professional potential. Until I began to work for myself, I was one of these women, either employed well below my skill level or underemployed, working part-time because that was all I could manage.

12

Neurodiversity and employment

Professor Amanda Kirby, CEO of Do-IT Solutions, a 'tech for good' company providing training and web-based tools to support neurodiverse people to gain and sustain employment and for employers to attract, retain and harness neurodiverse talent

Neurodiversity is about everyone's brains and how they differ. Some people have traits associated with conditions such as Autism Spectrum Disorder, Dyslexia, Developmental Coordination Disorder and ADHD. The reality is that no one fits into one neat box.

Many adults may have grown up struggling with socialising in school, reading and writing or with playing ball games and some will have been bullied. They may have been confused about the reasons for not quite fitting in and thought they had fewer capabilities than they actually had because of lower self-esteem.

There is extensive evidence that certain groups, in particular females, may have been missed or misdiagnosed.[73-82] For some, they may have been diagnosed with anxiety and depression. Much of the early research relating to neurodivergent conditions had in fact focused much more on males and so the vision of neurodiversity was tilted in that direction. We are only recognising this now as many more females are coming forward and being diagnosed and then starting to make sense of their childhood and for some adulthood as well.

Today we know that the 'conditions' and 'disorders' that have been categorised are in effect much more multi-dimensional and they all overlap or co-occur. This means the reality is that most people have strengths and challenges and a 'spiky profile'. It is these dips and peaks, the spikiness, that causes some people challenge as the way one person or another communicates with each other may differ and cause the clashes and confusion we sometimes see.

Awareness among educators and employers remain[s] relatively low in relationship to neurodiversity. Where training has been given it has often tended to be in silos. A more recent move on the parts of some employers to embracing complexity and taking a more person-centred approach is one that is welcomed.

There remain some challenges relating to the understanding of neurodiversity in relation to attracting, hiring and retaining talent in the workplace and the need to ensure anticipatory adjustments are in place to ensure [that] inclusion takes place at all stages from education and into employment is essential to ensure that Neurodiversity isn't another 'this year's campaign'.

7 Moving between difference and awareness

This chapter looks briefly at moving from an experience of difference to an awareness of that difference and asks you about your own experiences of being different.

7.1 Realising difference

Realising you are different can happen slowly, in pace with a burgeoning awareness of the lives around you, or in a single jolting event. It always happens in relation to an awareness of others, for how could you notice difference if you did not notice anyone outside of yourself? At first, you may simply be different, others may notice but you do not. Like me squinting and splintering the sun into rainbows in the playground.

Realising you are different can make you feel vulnerable. As social animals we get our protection from being within the herd. Noticing yourself to be other from the herd makes you feel unsafe. Animals that feel unsafe hide; in my case behind trees and inside locked toilet cubicles.

Once you have realised you are different, this differentness may become fundamental to your identity. As you define yourself in relation to the herd you build your otherness into the definition. You may seek to own it, as I did with my rejection of the things everyone else liked, or you may wish it were not so and take it on as a sense of shame.

7.2 Reflections on awareness

Everyone is unique, so everyone can identify with the feeling of being different to those around them.

Do you have particular memories that stand out to you as informing you of your difference?

Do you have memories that inform you not of your 'otherness' to those around you, but of your 'withness' with them, memories of times where you were a part of the action, embedded in the crowd, where you sang alongside the other voices, or were held up by them?

Where would you root your difference?

Did you have a different religion to those around you? Was it that your family makeup was different to that of your friends? Is your difference founded in money, were you richer or poorer than the herd? Is your difference physical, were you particularly tall, or was your hair a different colour?

If you find your difference located in how you connected socially with others, then you and I may have the same type of difference.

8   Diagnosis

This chapter describes how I came to be diagnosed as autistic. I moved from an awareness that I was autistic to a resolve to 'fix' my autism. Although at one point in my life I did consider myself to be 'fixed', what I had actually accomplished was competency at being able to hide, or mask, my autism. Later in life that mask was removed from me by someone very close to me, and as a result of this unveiling, I went first to the doctors and then to a psychologist for a full assessment of autism.

8.1 Fixing

When I was 11 years old I read an article in a magazine that described autism as a triad of deficits. Autistic people were socially deficient, they were no good at communicating and had no imagination. It is worth noting that the triad model has been updated since I read that article in the late 1980s, and that my understanding of what was written there was that of an 11 year old.

For a more contemporary, less deficit-based, rendering of autism consider Autistic UK's[83] outline of seven common characteristics shared by autistic people:

1. Different sensory experiences
2. Non-standard ways of learning and approaching problem solving
3. Deeply focused thinking and passionate interests in specific subjects

4. Atypical, sometimes repetitive, movement

5. Need for consistency, routine and order

6. Difficulties in understanding and expressing language as used in typical communication, both verbal and non-verbal

7. Difficulties in understanding and expressing typical social interaction.

In their description of these characteristics, Autistic UK point out the positive and negative effects of possessing such traits, rather than framing them solely and simplistically in the negative.

The article I read detailed what the life of a person with the outlined deficits might be like. In its description, I recognised myself. It was a very matter of fact recognition, an "Ah so that is what it is". I had been wondering.

The article described autism as a problem that needed fixing. So I duly set myself the task of fixing it. The article said I would struggle with imagination; I checked that one off the list immediately. I have always had a vivid and active imagination. In my head that was one down, just two more deficits to tackle: communication and making friends.

By the time I was 17, I considered myself to have caught up on the skills I previously lacked and so to be 'fixed'.

Unsurprisingly my 'fixing' had not actually changed my innate nature. Instead, I had incrementally mastered the art of masking.

8.2 Masking

Masking to some degree is what everyone does to integrate into society. Our teenage years are when we learn this performance most acutely; we give up the unguarded nature of childhood and we become socially hyper aware. We want to be liked, and we act accordingly.

In time we recognise that actually we are more likeable as ourselves. The model person held up by society as what we should be like, the template, cookie-cutter person, is not real. What we aim for is something in the middle. A true version of ourselves, but with some of the edges knocked off so as not to be so truthful as to get into trouble.

In particular situations we put on particular masks: how we behave in front of our boss is very different to how we behave in front of our family or our closest friends and so on.

It is easy to misunderstand autistic masking as the widely deployed social skill of getting along with others.

The difference between autistic masking and social masking comes in the evolution of the mask. Neurotypical people begin with a relatively convincing mask – the teenager will, more or less, wear the right clothes, name the right bands when asked what they like and so on: they will follow the herd. The new person in the office will mind their manners in front of their boss, but be the life and soul of the party when on a work night out with their colleagues. Over time these masks will thin a little, they are edited, and the real person begins to shine through.

People value authenticity enormously. As we grow older and mature, we understand and appreciate differences in others more. At college it was more okay to be weird than it was at school. And at university it was positively celebrated. In the world of getting along with one another the masks are worn initially but are gradually removed over time.

For autistic people, masking works in the other direction. The first masks are not very good, we do not know the right clothes to wear, we are unlikely to name the right celebrities when asked. We will be too honest and blunt in front of our bosses and we will not go on the work night out. Over time our masks change too, but instead of increased authenticity, instead of the masks thinning or slipping off, they get better and better: we become more convincingly 'normal'.

At least my mask did.

...Or perhaps I like to think it did.

Autistic maskers risk losing a sense of self behind the mask, risk losing their identity not just to the outside world but to themselves as well. As autistics strive to become the masked version of themselves, to embody the reality as it is seemingly 'meant' to be, they lose who they are. This can cause a lot of problems.

8.3 Unveiling

Eventually someone I loved very much shouted at me that there was something wrong with my head and I should get it fixed.

In my memory it was shouted, but in truth I expect the words were simply said with an enormous amount of emotion behind them, such that the shock of their impact registered as a shout.

I was deeply hurt and offended.

In my mind I had already fixed it. And I had taken a long time in doing so. I had worked really hard.

I had done it.

To be brutally honest, I was proud of the work I had done. Proud of the masking I could manifest. Having it pointed out as not enough felt churlish, as though I had walked a hundred miles only to be told I was a couple of minutes late.

The frustration was justified. They could see that we were both fighting to save a six-year-old love affair from giving way and breaking up our new little family. More than anything, my partner and I wanted our young son to grow up with a Mummy and a Daddy who lived under the same roof. A task our irreconcilable breakdown in communication ultimately saw us fail at. Failure did not come through a lack of effort. Neither one of us could *ever* be accused of not having tried. We fought until we were utterly defeated.

My partner agreed that I should explore diagnosis. He advised me to go to the doctor, not because he did not care about me but because he cared enormously about us. Out-of-kilter communication and an imperfect understanding of self can be masked reasonably well in public, but in private these things hurt those closest to you.

The frustration, despair and anger were all measures of how much the relationship meant. People do not get angry about things they do not care about.

How can you explain your side of things to someone who only sees their own version of events?

How can you believe a person to be capable of change when they insist it is you who should change?

How can someone explain who they are to you when they have not got an accurate view of themselves?

How can you understand someone's feelings if they do not know what they are themselves and do not display them as you display them?

How can you tell which bits of a well-honed mask are real and which are not?

How can you have a relationship with someone who is not fully there?

In the end I went to the doctor "to get fixed" because I wanted to make things right.

8.4 Going to the doctor

My initial indignant fury at the suggestion that I ought to get diagnosed saw me arrive at my GP's surgery in two frames of mind.

In part I marched in defiant. Yes, I was autistic, and I was there to claim the card that said so. I would wave that card in my partner's face and demand to be understood.

In part I slunk in with my tail between my legs to confess that this thing I had been trying to fix for more than two decades had not been fixed and was causing problems.

I took with me a collection of observations about why I thought I was autistic. The job I do has seen me support many autistic children through the years and my list was mainly populated by examples from my life that seemed to match with their lives, plus a few my partner insisted should be included.

- I hate wearing coats. Even in the rain, my skin is waterproof, I do not dissolve, so why should I wear a coat?

- Wearing shoes makes me feel claustrophobic. My job involves a lot of public speaking; I have it written into my contract that I will be allowed to present barefoot.

- When I do buy shoes, I buy them too big so that there is room in them to wiggle my toes. I go to extreme lengths to buy the same shoes over and over again, same make, same colour; alternatives are uncomfortable.

- I eat the same dinner every night. As a child I restricted what I ate to beige and ketchup. At university I lived off crisps and sweets. When I go out to dinner, I search for the same meal on the menu and get agitated if it is not there.

- Sometimes I find the world too real to move about in; the detail of it is overwhelming. I have been unable to climb a flight of stairs because the exposed brick wall at the top seemed to hold too much meaning. I have spent hours trying to look at more than one blade of grass, in no way able to deal with a whole lawn. I have gone around and around on the Circle Line because my fascination with the pattern on the floor held me hostage. Some hotel carpets make me dizzy.

  At times the visual detail of the world is a strength; at six years old I found the pin from a watch strap lost on a football field. I can be relied upon to find the lost back of an earring in any given situation.

- I cannot break rules. I will not let the dog off the lead if a sign says not to, even if every other walker we pass has their dog roaming free. I will not stop on a double yellow line, not even to pause with the engine still running so someone can dart out to post a letter.

- I sense pain and temperature differently to the people I know. I fill baths from only the hot tap, and afterwards my skin takes hours to return to its usual hue. Sometimes if I have had a bath before bed, I can still see the red tidemarks on my legs in the morning.

- I had a cough for most of my adolescence. I was tested for asthma but my lungs were fine. It was described as a nervous tic. When it went away, I began displaying motor tics when tired.

- I take things literally. I always find the signs on doors that say 'This door is alarmed' amusing; poor door, I think, I wonder what shocked it so?

- I have a right and wrong way to do everything, from moral conduct all the way down to how to eat a digestive biscuit.

I am distressed if once I have explained to someone close to me the right way to do something, and why it is the right way, they do not do that thing right.

- When plans change, my head stays fixed on the old plan. Even when the changes are good.

- I do not 'get over' things quickly enough and I do not make 'the right' facial expressions.

I am used to not being able to express myself clearly at doctors' appointments. I too easily fall into the pattern of answering questions with what I think is the right answer, rather than trying to find the words to express particular symptoms or concerns. So I took the list in the form of a letter which I handed over awkwardly to the doctor as I sat down.

My doctor read the letter, nodded and then asked me if I would be willing to complete a couple of simple check-box tests. I was given a sheet of paper with questions and a pencil. Answer: "sometimes, often, rarely, never". I checked the relevant boxes.

My score was counted and because I passed, or because I failed, a second piece of paper was produced, and again I answered, "sometimes, often, rarely, never".

These were the AQ and EQ assessments which are a part of the Adult Asperger Assessment.[84] AQ stands for Autistic Spectrum Quotient, a measure from 1 to 50 of, presumably, how autistic a person is. A score of more than 32 on the AQ is considered to indicate that a person has Asperger's. I scored 41. EQ stands for Empathy Quotient: on this test, a score under 30 is considered to indicate Asperger's. I scored 15.

The doctor totted up my scores and told me that what I had answered indicated that it was likely that I was autistic, and he would refer me to a team of specialist psychologists for further assessment.

As he spoke, my eyes were on my son, who was not yet two years old and had for the duration of the appointment sat beautifully on a chair beside me reading a small cardboard book to himself. The doctor followed my gaze. "But don't worry", he said, "you are clearly an excellent mother."

His words struck me cold.

At no point had I considered that going for an autism assessment might entail any assessment of my fitness to be a parent. And although in his words he clearly indicated that there were no concerns about my parenting, that it had crossed his mind at all rattled me.

If I had been there for another test, a test for cancer let's say, and having checked the mole on my skin, the doctor had said he would refer me to specialists to get it checked. If my eyes had settled on my son then, would he still have said, "But do not worry, you are clearly an excellent mother"?

I went home, feeling part vindicated, part ashamed of the outcome of the appointment. "I am being referred," I reported.

"Good," came the reply.

In their eyes, I was being dealt with, my wonky thinking and unhelpful point of view would be ironed out.

In my eyes, an explanation would be given and they would be forced to understand things from my perspective.

Neither of us won any points for understanding or empathy that day.

8.5 Going to the clinical psychologist

A few weeks later, I went for the first of what was to be a series of in-depth interviews with a clinical psychologist. Stepping into the psychologist's room was a glimpse of what a different world might look like. There was no expectation of eye contact. When I removed my shoes, before tucking my legs under me on the chair, there was no sense that this was peculiar behaviour. "Is everything in here okay for you?" she asked, "would you like me to adjust the lighting at all?"

I realised that the offer was genuine. As a rule, I find day-to-day life a little too bright, so I requested that the blinds be adjusted and they were. I sat in a room that was visually gentle for me. If I am standing and talking to someone at work or at a social gathering, unless I concentrate, I find I rotate my body so that it is at a 90 degree angle to theirs. I am habituated to the concentration that it takes to maintain a semblance of face-to-faceness when conversing. But in this room, there was no need. I sat facing 90 degrees away from the psychologist and this was fine.

The lack of effort it took to converse was remarkable to me. How much easier the world would be if it was always a shade or too dimmer, my shoes were off and instead of the confrontational face to face, the more companionable (in my perspective) side by side was the standard remit for conversation.

Coming back out into the 'real' world afterwards was quite a jolt. I was suddenly more aware of all the effort I was making – the multitude of tiny little adjustments I make continuously when with people in order to be as I am supposed to be.

In addition to interviewing me, the psychologist interviewed some of my close friends and family members. I was shocked by some of the contributions these people made to my assessment. In particular, my mother recalling that as a baby I would tense up if she tried to cuddle me, and that as a very young child I pushed physical affection away. My own son was nearing two years of age. Two years of endless cuddles, still often carried on my hip, falling asleep on my shoulder in that dream of trusting flesh that only the very young offer. I could not fathom how hurtful it would have been for me if instead of curling himself into me warm and soft, he had pushed me away. Yet apparently this was what I had done.

I apologised to my mother. She said there was no need. I was her first child, she said at the time she had not known differently, it was only when my sister came along two and a half years later that she noticed. As we grew up, my sister was always described to people as "a very cuddly child". I had always thought that this was something exceptional about my sister; now I recognise it was a contrast with me that was being articulated. Since getting diagnosed, I hug my mother more often than I used to. I am trying to make it up to her.

9 The report

This chapter is included for reasons of openness. It details my personal diagnosis. Whether you are neurotypical or whether you are autistic, you may find that you have traits in common with me. You are more likely to have traits in common with me if you are autistic, but what is outlined here is not a description of autism. It is specific to me: this is my own little pixel on the colour wheel of the autistic spectrum.

To write this I had to re-read the report I received upon diagnosis. Four years on from when I first read it, I still found it to be a dense and heavy read. Compressed into its 16 pages is a liturgy of all the things I have struggled with or failed to do through the years.

Meeting the challenges reported on one by one in my life, I have always optimistically imagined that one day I will get the hang of them. Perhaps by the next time a particular foible pops up to thwart me, I will have worked out a way of circumnavigating it. However, seeing them all laid out on the report's pages, it is easy to track the continuous and unchanging nature of my autistic traits. The circumstances in which I come up against them change, the background to each challenge is different, the people involved change, but the underlying cause of the difficulties remains the same. It is very sobering for me to reflect that the cause of my difficulties is me.

The diagnosis document tells me that the problems I have encountered are not caused by a failure of effort on my part, which is heartening. But it also tells me that exerting effort in the future is unlikely to bear fruit. I am not going to change. This is fundamentally how I am. If I accept the difference, then I may end up less exhausted, but I do not get to not be different.

9.1 A grown-up child

The report states that as a child I was described as being "fiercely independent, bright, creative, early to walk and talk". During their interviews, members of my family recounted my childhood catch phrase: "I'll do it myself". My mother explained that I have always preferred to tackle things on my own, rejecting help and instruction. A peer from school described me to the psychologist as having been "different to other children, overly adult in mannerisms and very serious, with a keen sense of right and wrong". In chatting to me about the report, my mother told me: "Childhood was always an afront to your dignity."

Autistic children are recognised in research as being "less accepted by peers and hav[ing] fewer reciprocal friendships" (personal comment by my mother; see also [85]). Researchers[86] note that autistic girls often prefer the company of older or younger people who are either more understanding or less demanding than same-age peers. At this time in my life, I would have fitted that description perfectly, avoiding peer contact at school, seeking out adults to chat to, and sometimes at home dominating play between my little sister and her friends.

My sister remembers being afraid of the world I inhabited, believing that to grow up would mean having to contend with the social situations I experienced. "Through you," she told me, "I learned the social world was a hostile place, full of rules you do not know which can change at any moment. And you live under the constant threat of being revealed." Happily for her, this fearful social landscape did not materialise in her growing up.

All my school reports comment on my maturity; In my teachers' eyes I was a little grown-up, preferring the company and conversation of adults over peers. I was quiet and studious and got good grades. But in other ways, the label of 'mature' did not match up.

I did not date, or express an interest in doing so as my peers matured. I spent a lot of time collecting small items. I collected pencil leads and carried with me a collection of hundreds of them in different colours which I would inspect during lessons. I also collected the small balls found at the end of ink cartridges for fountain pens. I collected small fuzzy plastic bears. I collected a great many things. I would have told you proudly at the time that I collected collections. I did not allow my parents, in particular my mother, to go out in the evenings. On the rare occasions that they did, I reacted by crying hysterically; the sort of reaction you might expect from a toddler, but one I performed until well into my teens. (This sort of reaction is one Rowe[87] reflects on briefly as being a part of autistic separation anxiety.) Although I expressed great anxiety and great fear, I was unable to talk about my emotions and did not show the awareness of them that you might expect from an adolescent.

9.2 Emotions

TW

The report documents me as someone whose emotional processing works differently to the expected norm. My mother testifies that as a child: "Joanna seemed to find it virtually impossible to find words to express her feelings. She was unwilling, or unable to identify and communicate emotions." She later explained to me the frustration she felt when "I could see something was clearly wrong, and your mouth would move as if you wanted to tell me, but no words would come out." (It is common for autistics to experience alexithymia: difficulties verbally describing subjective emotional experiences. See pop out box 31: 'Autistic emotional processing and research bias' for more information.)

This failure of emotional literacy runs through the years, having all sorts of consequences. On record are periods of depression and two breakdowns. These are attributed by the psychologist to social exhaustion. She goes on to observe that they are likely to have been exacerbated by my lack of awareness of my own feelings. Had I been aware that I was getting stressed, or feeling low, I might have been able to take remedial steps before feelings ran so high that they overwhelmed me.

The psychologist comments on my having "rigid rules around emotions"; some are permitted, some are not. She also reports the frustration of my partner and of myself with my inability to communicate an emotional response to any given situation. My partner always understood this to be evidence of a lack of trust – "Why won't you tell me what you feel?" – and was hurt by it. Understandably so. My own frustrations are documented on my body in scars on my arms, hands and chest from acts of self-harm.

I want to be clear about how hidden these aspects of my personality are on a day-to-day basis. Written out here in a block, it could be easy for a reader to imagine me as lost in a world of emotional confusion. In life most people meet me as a happy, emotionally steady, down to earth person. In daily life it can actually help to not be too aware of my feelings; I can focus on a task without being swayed by the ebb and flow of a rich emotional life.

Over the last ten years of working for myself, travelling nationally (and occasionally internationally) delivering training to parents and professionals who support people with complex disabilities, I have met thousands upon thousands of people. I have provided guidance for parents and professionals who are struggling, I have challenged people to up their game in terms of the support they provide. I have contributed to policy and influenced practice. In all this time, and in all these conversations, my self-harm scars have been noticed only once and that was by the father of an autistic teenage girl who had herself begun to self-harm the very week of our meeting.

In addition, only once in all my time on the road professionally (and bearing in mind that many of the conferences I present at are about inclusive education and are attended by experts in the field of special educational needs), have I been 'spotted' as being autistic. The person who identified my autism without my disclosing it just so happened to be Professor Barry Carpenter, one of the lead authors on NASEN's guide to supporting autistic girls: 'Girls and autism: Flying under the radar'.[71]

A lack of emotional awareness is not the same as a lack of emotions. I recognise emotions in others and connect with them strongly. I am often moved to tears by stories I read or see. Reflecting on these moments, I can acknowledge that my emotional connectedness is often in response to what could be described as easy to understand situations: for example, a person's relationship breaking down, or someone being critically ill. In more nuanced situations within my own relationships, I do less well at identifying and empathising with the emotions of my partner.

I often think that the problem is that when someone is very close to me, I treat them as I treat myself. I apply the same strict emotional rules that I apply to myself to them and, it would appear, the same level of emotional awareness.

The report also details what are perceived as "disproportionate reactions" with regard to other people's suffering. I adopt other people's problems as my own; in my mind they hold equal import-ance. The psychologist notes that I feel the problems of others "to an overwhelming extent" and in doing so, I take on responsibility for lives and struggles which are not my own.

The report acknowledges that this difference can be viewed positively: "this level of care and concern for others can clearly be seen as a strength and has undoubtedly contributed to the admir-able work Joanna is engaged in". The report goes on to warn, how-ever, that this 'over feeling', for want of a better description, could pose a risk to me in the long term.

The report also documents times when my emotional responses have been wrong; for example, I got angry at my partner for being ill, considering it to be their fault. Responses like that cannot in any way be viewed as a strength.

9.3 Social skills

I have always been able to explain away the social mismatch between myself and my peers for any stage of life:

> As a toddler, I would have said it was due to my different living circumstances (I lived on a boat not in a house).

As a child, I would have said it was a lack of shared cultural capital (I did not watch television; the other children did).

As a teenager, I might have told you it was because their interests were silly (why would you waste your brain memorising statistics about a boy band?)

In my twenties, it was because I moved back to Cornwall as a graduate when most of my fellow graduates stayed in their university towns.

In my thirties...

By this point, I might have begun to acknowledge that my excuses were wearing thin.

The report clearly outlines my social failings through the years:

The toddler identified as atypical by playground staff for standing rooted to the spot and not playing. My mother reported that I "struggled to integrate socially" and that I was, in this way, different to my sister (who also lived on a boat and grew up with very little exposure to television but who has always had a close circle of friends around her).

The primary school child who hid through playtimes and engaged in what the report calls stereotypical behaviours, but the autistic community would refer to as stimming: some people flap, some jump, I span.

The socially isolated, studious secondary school student who had no shared interests with her peers and focused obsessively on a single friendship.

At college, the report notes that although I had been introduced to a network of friends, I rarely attended social events: house parties, college balls, etc. At this time, I referred to myself as an "observer" of the social life of my peers, I did not view myself as participating.

At university, I was at first reclusive and then later on heavily involved with a particular society, but still did not socialise with members of this society outside of its weekly meetings.

At work, the difference between my social skills and those of colleagues was noted in my annual performance management reviews. I was set a target of improving my connection with other members of the team. I was advised to socialise more, instructed that I should spend more time in the staffroom during breaks, and should attend work nights out.

The target to better integrate myself socially with my work colleagues remained on my performance management review for two years running because, despite considerable effort on my part, I failed to meet it the first year. The report notes that I was bullied at work, but did not recognise that the bully's behaviour was inappropriate until informed by managers that what they had witnessed constituted a sackable offence.

9.3.1 Perspective on 'success'

The psychologist writing the report notes the idiosyncratic way in which I described my social successes to her. In my mid-twenties (considerably later than my peers who all tackled this challenge at an age when it was still illegal for them to buy alcohol), I decided to go night-clubbing. The psychologist quotes me saying that I made a "considerable effort" to do this, practising for weeks in advance, planning where to go and what to do, rehearsing for the event. When I went, I went on my own. I drank only water. I danced for five hours in the same spot at the same time every week. Eventually I was offered a job as a podium dancer and took that as a sign that I had (in my words) "mastered" clubbing. Shortly after "achieving" (again this is the word I used in my description) clubbing, I ceased to go anymore.

I guess someone else explaining their adventures in nightlife might tell tales of drunken nights and romantic escapades, they might say things like they "enjoyed" clubbing, or "had a lot of fun". They probably would not view it as a ladder of achievement and celebrate reaching the top. This particular social success was perhaps not the accomplishment of normal I considered it to be at the time.

9.4 Forming relationships

The report describes how I have made friendships through studying particular people, to a level described as "obsessive". The psychologist notes that "Joanna has clearly managed to sustain a small number of very close friendships using these methods", and that my friends (those previously studied and obsessed over) have described me as "exceptionally loyal".

The report suggests that I may have found close relationships harder to master than friendships because of a lack of study materials. Close observation of the internal workings of successful partnerships is hard to achieve unless one is within that partnership itself.

I am described as "not really believing" that people think differently to me. This is noted as a contributory factor to the misunderstandings and miscommunications common within my relationships, as is my disconnected or overly connected emotional response to events.

9.5 Communication

The report documents my ongoing social communication differences: that I do not naturally make eye contact, that my body language can come across as overly formal, that friends and family had reported my facial expressions as being misleading. The psychologist notes that I have clearly made "considerable efforts to learn about social rules and to emulate social behaviours".

During our interviews, the psychologist asked me if I had ever researched this topic. I told her about the body language books I read in my teens and the way I chose, and continue to choose, to watch television programmes that focus on relationships between people so that I can study the interactions. It was not until she asked the question that I considered that perhaps not every teenager studies body language from books borrowed from the library.

9.5.1 Communication in context

The report documents situations in which I found relating to others easier. A pattern is identified which I had not previously noticed: in situations where I have a clear role, I function better.

At school, given the job of supervising the computer room at playtimes I connected with others.

As a teacher in front of a class I relate playfully to my students.

As a new mum, I initially floundered at toddler groups, unable to chat to the other mothers, adrift in a totally unfamiliar social environment and exhausted from the sleepless nights associated with early parenthood. But when the leader of the group I attended quit and a volunteer was required to take their place, I took on the role and, with one or two notable hiccups aside, once in place talked confidently to the other parents and provided support.

(My experience of coping better with social situations in which I had a clear role to play is echoed by pop out box 2 part 1: 'Jeremey: I think I am autistic but I do not want to be diagnosed'.)

9.5.2 Communication within relationships

The report reads: Joanna "communicates better in writing" (Let's hope so, hey?); "struggles to understand other people's interest in chit chat she deems pointless"; "has a set of pre-prepared questions and responses that enable her to blend in"; and "has never really shared interests in common with peers".

Friends who were interviewed in conjunction with my diagnosis observed that my conversation topic choices were often inappropriate, and my input into their conversations could also be out of kilter with the flow of the conversation or overly blunt. Work colleagues described my contributions to conversations as "random".

With regard to my intimate relationships, the report documents that I struggle to put myself into another's shoes in order to anticipate and predict thoughts and behaviours. It notes that I often fail to pick up on the non-verbal clues which inform meaning and intent, and that my partner found me to be blunt, snappy and rude in my manner of communication.

The report describes me as "enormously tired" by the continuous communication difficulties experienced within my relationship. Many of the difficulties I experienced at the time of diagnosis stemmed from disagreements over what was meant by something that had been said. The report acknowledges that my partner at the time and I had gone through a long, painful (and ultimately flawed) process of negotiation, agreeing to be very explicit with each other within our communications: we had agreed to state the intended meaning of our words alongside whatever we said. (It did not work out as we hoped it might.)

9.6 Fixed and focused thinking

Intense is a word that has always described me. The report observes that when something captures my interest, I tend "to explore this exhaustively" and devote myself to it "with an unusual intensity". The psychologist lists examples from the interviews she had conducted: reading each of Roald Dahl's books 30 to 40 times before moving on to other literature; standing in the playground repeating the words of a two-hour-long story tape to myself; and various other projects which have over the years captured my attention.

My "strong preference for routine and sameness" is noted along with observations about my eating the same dinner every night and finding surprises – however pleasant in their content – to be distressing. It is observed that I express a preference for the routine of weekdays over the more free-flowing nature of weekends, and that I do "not see the value in doing something just once". When plans change, "Joanna cannot get over the stated plans not being carried out".

The psychologist explores my need for control, explaining that:

> Joanna has a strong need for predictability and to feel in control. She has never been drunk for this reason. Her partner reports that midwives attending the birth of her first son

commented that they had never encountered a woman so in control of her body.

My thinking is described as being black and white, and it is noted that I spend a lot of time considering what is right and what is wrong and am very bothered by people who appear to be content with things being 'okay' or 'good enough'. The report explains that I get very stressed if it is suggested I have broken a rule, "even where there is no consequence and the rule is obviously not in use". And that I over apply the concept of right and wrong to many daily tasks: the right way to put a knife on the draining board, the right way to eat a biscuit. I am recorded as reporting that I feel "deeply hurt" and "offended" when people do not follow rules after I have explained them.

A contrast is drawn between my rule-following mind and its applicability to the social world:

> Joanna has an unusually strong drive and ability to systemise. She has applied this to learning rules of socialising, however she has inevitably found it very difficult to develop rules she can rely on that would be able to accommodate the many nuances of social interaction and inherent unpredictability of the social world.

9.7 Reflection: a mosaic

The report ends with advice and offers of counselling and access to therapies – tying in nicely with the understanding of my 11-year-old self and that of my partner at the time: that autism is something that needs fixing.

When I first received the report, I was surprised at how it differed from the list I took with me to the appointment that began my pathway to diagnosis. There was so much more in it that I had not been aware of. Every item on my list and everything detailed in the report could, on their own, be explained without reference to autism. There is no one thing I can point to and say, "*that* is autism".

When I first began tentatively to mention being autistic publicly, one of the ways in which I did this was through an album of photographs entitled *Spectrum Shards*. Each photo in that album was a little piece of my autism. Perhaps the photo album shards, the items on my list, and the bigger topics laid out in the report would be better understood as a mosaic. It is the picture they paint when considered as a whole that is autism, not any one piece within that image. As with a mosaic, the image of autism can be put together in a great many ways, hence the experience of autism being a spectrum one.

I may have traits in common with other autistics and indeed with neurotypical people, but individual traits are not definitive. To define autism, you have to step away from the minute pieces of the mosaic and regard the whole. When you do this, the communality of experience between autistics, and between neurotypicals, is rendered clear.

10 Blog part one: the first weeks after diagnosis

Post-diagnosis, I began to anonymously blog and post on social media about being autistic. I often write to clarify my own understanding of a subject and writing in this semi-public way meant I could benefit from other people's insights as well as learning how other people responded to the new understanding of self I was trying on.

In Chapter 3, I outlined a journey envisaged as stops along a railway line that began with not knowing you are autistic and ended with adopting an autistic identity. In beginning my blog and setting up those anonymous social media accounts, I was effectively boarding that metaphorical train and heading towards the stops of awareness and understanding.

My relative willingness to start that journey stands in contrast to other people's experiences of the same opportunity; for example, Jeremey (box 2 part 1), Noleta (box 1), my father (box 4) and the college students (box 10).

The segments in this chapter of the book are essentially the online diary I kept of my first few weeks post-identification. You will notice that my attention is on trying to explain what the diagnosis means when I clearly do not fully understand it myself.

I have tried to keep the posts as they were originally written online. That said, a few changes have been made for print. I have corrected typos and altered sentences which were hard to understand. I have cut out chunks of waffle. In places, pictures added insight to the text and I have been unable to add these here; where their absence left a hole, I have added a few words to paper over the gap. In all cases, the original essence and tone of these anonymously posted blogs have been retained – however uncomfortable doing this has made me feel.

There was no imagined reader for these words. I posted them into the ether of the internet without a guarantee of a response, and unsure if I would want one at all. I left them there online to see what would become of them. My voice in these posts is unedited and honest.

10.1 Does this suit me?

My diagnosis is like a new outfit; a bold new outfit.

Do I look great in this? As great as I felt in the privacy of the changing rooms?

Will I walk tall, an extra bit of bounce in my stride? Or will stepping into the outside world make me realise that my own taste is not what I thought it was? Will I long to be hidden in the changing room? Or to be dressed back in my old, not quite right, but not so obvious, tatty clothes?

On the day I got diagnosed, I came home, to raised eyebrows: "Well?"

"I have autism."

"Autism? Don't you mean Asperger's?"

My diagnosis is Asperger's, a part of the Autistic spectrum. But it feels a bit like a first-class carriage on a train, my inclination is to say Autistic and be grouped with a broader collective. I do not want to set myself apart from peers whom others might want to be distinguished from.

It is humbling in a useful way, to suddenly be given a tool to use to see how my interpretation of things may not be accurate. Not because I am either right or wrong, but because, apparently, not all things are either right or wrong.

As I recognise the diagnostic classic of binary thinking in myself I find it gently funny. It is so obviously there through all my thoughts how come I did not spot it before? It is a bit like discovering I do not have free will, all these uniqueness[es], oddities, peculiarities right through my life are actually spelled out in a document that unites me with

81

a whole bunch of other peculiar folk. I was not *me* at all. I was simply one of these.

I worry about adding my voice to those already populating the autistic world, from glimpses on Twitter I have encountered people with fixed world views, convinced they are right, speaking on behalf of other people with fixed world views who think they are wrong. It looks like dangerous waters, I might just paddle for a while in my new outfit and my mixed metaphors.

10.2 Week one wobbles

I have set this blog up and closed it down several times. My doing that mirrors my response to knowing I am autistic.

In some senses I have known since I was 11 and first read what it meant to be autistic. In the intervening years between then and my diagnosis I have worked hard to learn everything I need in order to be neurotypical. Although things remained different for me than they were for other people I did not feel my difference had an impact on my life.

Certain, hard, private events held my nose to the glass and forced me to look and to see, that I am autistic, and ever will be. The permanence of it cannot be gotten away from. So I set up this blog to think about it. And then took it down, deciding not to think. Set it up again as I was still thinking. Took it down because I do not want to think about it, does thinking about it make it real or is it real anyway?

Here is something I wrote out of notes scribbled when the blog was down:

Dot to dot – or caught in a net?

As part of the diagnostic process I wrote a list of all my strangenesses: four pages of bullet points. I handed them to the assessing psychiatrist saying, "Here's a list of all my failings" to which she responded with something suitably diplomatic.

It is a list of everything I could not do when other people could, and seemingly so easily too. It is a list of things I have struggled with that should not be difficult. Of things I do not understand that everyone else does.

When I got the diagnosis that list of bullet points became a dot-to-dot picture and the diagnosis joined all of those dots up and made a picture of autism, and they weren't my fault any more. I did not fail at those things because I was bad, or not as ... clever ... strong ... astute ... as my peers. I failed at those things because I am different, not worse. And had the people doing those things so effortlessly been different too they might also have failed. It was not me.

The diagnosis was a relief. As daft and as small as some of those things are, they have been carried with me all this time, so that when I put pen to paper, I can come up with a four-page list in a matter of minutes. Suddenly they made sense and a weight was lifted. They were not because of *me*, they were because of autism.

But even as I first thought that it did not quite sit right. In an era of people-first language, "A person with X condition", people with autism are famously prone to condition-first language, "I am autistic." It is a positive thing in that to them autism is clearly a community, something to which they belong and with which they identify, as you would with a culture or a nation. So can I say it was not me, it was the autism? Are not the two things the same?

As the week rolled on, I began to realise that it was not just the dots on my list that were connected by the diagnosis. My sense of humour was in there too, and my work ethic, and my ability to be creative and to see things in a different way to other people. The nice dot-to-dot picture became a net scooping up things I *wanted* to claim as mine. I am quite happy to think that I have got poor social skills because of a neurological condition, but I would also quite like to think that my strong work ethic is down to a rich vein of moral fibre running through my being and not a happenstance of that same neurological condition.

Drat! It would seem I cannot pick and choose which bits of me are autistic and which bits are not, it appears it is an all in/all out kind of an affair.

10.3 Telling people

In the main I remain in the neurotypical closet. I am not 'out' as autistic. But I feel I owe an explanation to some people for whom knowing about my diagnosis may help to make a certain sense of our shared past. My current partner explained it as being like a product recall on a faulty device: "You may have experienced some difficulties with this item, please rest assured that this was not the fault of the operator but appears to be caused by the wiring of the product which was not as advertised."

I did not expect the responses I got.

I told an old close friend, with whom I had had an intense friendship for more than a decade. "No, you are not," they said, "You are warm and friendly and engaging."

I realised I was being given an insight into the prejudice and ignorance that surrounds autism.

I told my ex-husband. A lovely man who more than any other deserves an explanation. In our marriage he adjusted his behaviour to suit my way of doing things. Adapting to me until he, the man I fell in love with, became invisible. And at the weekends, in the evenings, because I prefer to spend time on my own, absorbed in my own pursuits, he took to his workshop and created beautiful sculptures. Until...

Well ... to be in a relationship with a person, you have to spend time with them. So until, in the end, 'we' were gone.

He looked through the comprehensive report, which as well as detailing all the foibles I knew about covered a fair few more that I had not been aware of. He folded it neatly on the table, put his hand over it. "Do not apologise to me for any of these things. What you have here is a list of all the things that are brilliant about you. These are the things that make you you, and make you so wonderful. Do not change."

13

Defending the reality of a condition

Jayne Johnston, blogger at https://squarepeggee. blogspot.com, inclusive education professional and lover of: being outside; being upside down; and dancing

The response of others to a revelation that I need to live my life differently from the way they live theirs is varied. When you can't use a pretty x-ray picture to explain your differences, you can't count on an understanding response, or even a believing one.

Listening, accepting and accommodating is ideal. But it's not just that the alternatives are "less than ideal" – they are immeasurably harmful to the core of a person (not to mention to society in general, but that's a whole other topic!): their beliefs about themselves and thus their quality of life, and ultimately often their willingness to be alive.

If you are brave enough to declare, "I need to live my life this way" (and bear in mind it is likely to have been a long and terrifying road to reach this point) and are met with, "no, you don't" or "you shouldn't", what does that do to you?

Being told you're wrong, or selfish, or lazy, or greedy, for living the way you need to (be that taking down-time, taking a variety of medications, not working or working part-time, receiving benefits, using a wheel-chair when you can sometimes stand or walk, eating sufficient meals four to six times daily and having treats, insisting on written communication to support verbal, lying in bed more than whatever number of hours or days is deemed "acceptable", the list really could be endless – these are just some from experience within my family of a few of the adjustments we need for conditions including autism, ME/CFS, eating disorders, rheumatoid arthritis, depression) destroys you in more than just the obvious ways.

When people disbelieve your condition, they are effectively calling you a liar (or really stupid, depending on whether they think you believe what you are saying or not). The hard work you put in to manage all that you do is not only discounted, but used as ammunition against you to "prove" that you can actually cope "normally".

The denial of the condition results in both an actual immediate misunderstanding of your character, which is upsetting and isolating, but also a long-term wearing away of your beliefs about yourself. You begin to accept the shame cast upon you for not living like others. You are the Wrong kind of person. It likely resonates with the core beliefs that made it so hard to accept your condition and your needs in the first place, so your brain registers it as familiar and it sticks like Velcro rather than sliding off like Teflon (which is what our brains are programmed to do with ideas that don't agree with our beliefs). If you want a broader idea of how it feels to be disbelieved, just look up the effects of shame.

It is not just about living differently. People can deny that you experience the world differently, or that your experience of being alive is different from theirs (and they can do this implicitly or explicitly). You can't find that smell intolerable because I like it. You can't experience constant pain because I can't imagine that existence. Your condition can't be variable – do you have it or don't you? And the cycle of invalidation, isolation, believing you are not acceptable, continues. You start to question your own sensory experiences – if nobody else can see it, it can't be true...

When experience is denied there is no acknowledgement of a need for ways to cope. The lack of acceptance, by self or other, disables you beyond the primary effects of your differences. Mental health will inevitably take the toll.

There is one last effect that I don't want to forget about, which regards our own understanding of ourselves and our needs. When perceived as able or not having difficulties, no suggestions are made to help someone cope. Not only are needs not accommodated or adjustments made that could facilitate a fuller life, the person with the condition may be completely unaware that such accommodations or adjustments exist or could apply to them.

Many autistic people, for example, think in a distinctly black and white manner. This is why I chose to seek a formal diagnosis – I could not authorise myself to apply "autism things" to myself unless I "knew" I was autistic. But seven years later I am still discovering many ways in which I can make my life easier. Even after diagnosis, I either thought I didn't need them, so hadn't bothered to try them, or I didn't even know they were an option. Just as I didn't see myself in "that" box, neither did anybody supporting me. In fact, nobody trained was supporting me because we didn't realise I had support needs. I cannot overstate my gratitude for seven months in an unusually aware and accepting environment that has given me a foundation to start changing those beliefs about myself that I was overtly or covertly fed for so many years.

Rachel Barker also talks about what it feels like to have to defend the reality of a diagnosis in pop out box 20: 'Coming out experiences'.

14
Gaslighting

TW

Gaslighting is a term used to describe the psychological manipulation of another person such that they doubt their own reality. Jayne's reflections in pop out box 13 on defending the reality of a condition others doubted, resonate with what many other writers have written with regard to the gaslighting of the autistic community. To highlight just a few: Terra Vance[88] writes in The NeuroClastic about the 50 ways society gaslights and stonewalls autistic people; autistic international speaker and consultant Ann Memmott[89] blogged about the sustained gaslighting of autistic people; Anna Kennedy OBE interviewed Joely Williams[90] for the open access journal *Psychreg* about the gaslighting she experienced as an autistic woman growing up; and Seventh Voice[91] writes specifically about the gaslighting of women and girls on the autistic spectrum.

A quick glance across the internet at the voices of autistic people is enough to tell you that the experience of not having your reality believed by others is common to the experience of being autistic. That this gaslighting happens through ignorance of diversity, rather than through malign intent, makes little difference to the effect it has on those led by it to doubt their own lived experience.

10.4 You do not seem autistic

TW

I have upped who I tell, from people whose lives have been directly affected by my autism to a random selection of people, or should I call them test subjects, picked from different parts of my life, some friends but not close friends, others people I work with, or people I meet at groups I attend.

"I couldn't tell."

"But you don't seem autistic."

"No, you are not, you are fine."

These things are always meant as a compliment. Or as reassurance that perhaps the diagnosis is a mistake and someone with a magic wand will take away all the things that earned me that bit of paper.

When they respond this way, I feel it as a loss. It took me a while to work out why. Actually, it took me a while to work out what I felt, often it takes me a while to understand what it is [that] I am feeling.

The reason I feel it as a loss is because it lacks a recognition of the effort I go to in order to appear so ordinary to them.

A connection on Twitter got it, their first response was: "God you must be so exhausted with being so normal all the time." I knew what I felt then: gratitude!

And a not so close friend, who may become a closer friend, got it too, saying: "Does it make it all fall into place for you?" She was talking about the dot-to-dot picture I described before. "That is how it was for me," she continued, "when I was diagnosed as Dyslexic, suddenly all this stuff made sense."

I wonder how life would have been different if I had *seemed* autistic to people?

To my mind, I think I *did* seem pretty autistic at school. I did not make friends with my peers. I stood in the playground and spun [around]. I stood at one end of my nursery and looked at the bricks, they looked like my Lego bricks at home, only different. I did not know how to play with them. At primary school, I developed an obsession with a girl I wanted to be friends with. At secondary school, I locked myself in toilet cubicles away from peers at breaktimes. I was consistently moderately bullied. I spoke to adults, not children. I was clever, serious, disconnected.

What if someone had seen these things and realised I needed help making the connections that others made so easily, navigating the social landscape that others seem to have an inbuilt sat-nav for?

It is hard to think these what-ifs. I categorically do not want to think them because this was the hand I was dealt and I am fine with it. I do not want it to change. But if you asked me going forwards, what I would want to happen for a child like me going through the education system now ... for all that my struggling bore fruit, I would want them to have a smoother route. Because it also squashed stuff inside of me. And I do not think that achievement requires suffering.

I imagine it is possible to be a high flyer and to have had a smoother life. And not just for that person, but for those around them. What mother or father wants to send their child to a school where they know they will be sad and frightened? Even if you said, look, this sadness now will be the seeds of their later brilliance, I do not think it is an education system many would sign up to.

Teachers saw my academic intelligence in the classroom but did not see my lack of social intelligence.

Playground assistants shooed me away because they found my inability to play mildly frustrating; it meant they could not chat free of young ears.

If I had been more of a problem to them, if I had *seemed* more autistic, perhaps I would have been helped.

And now?

Now there is help I can have.

I can tell my child's nursery that because I have autism, I find talking on the phone difficult and I would prefer they emailed me. I have requested this twice in the past, but I bet now with the diagnosis they would be right on it. It feels like a power, one I am not sure I should use.

If I am ever employed again (I work for myself now after over a decade of failing to cope with working alongside colleagues), I can have a letter sent to my place of employment explaining what adjustments they should make for me.

And smaller things, just to myself, that power is there: I find sunlight too bright, does the diagnosis justify the buying of sunglasses?

In the past few weeks, I have realised I have been articulating things like the sun being too bright more than I ever used to. I have felt more able to be normal. And by that I do not mean be neurotypical, I mean more able to present myself as I am.

In beginning to talk about these things I realise I am opening a flood gate. There are so many things to say. I do so much to appear neurotypical. And now I am allowed to say that I am doing it. And in saying it, in recognising it myself, I get a sense of 'wow I am doing a lot'. Previously I have not thought about it, just got on with it, because it is what everyone does, isn't it? Isn't it? No one else seems tired, so I should just get on with it.

The people at the top of this post with their different reactions, I do not mind any of them, I am not sure I [would] have known what to say. I am interested only in my side of it, how the things they say make me feel. But for the record I think a good response would be, for me, for people to ask:

"What does the diagnosis mean for you?"

That is a safe neutral response.

10.5 I am autistic: I am English

I have autism. Where? At home? In a box somewhere? In my handbag?

I am a person with autism – autism accompanies me like a chaperone?

I am autistic – what my whole self, my whole identity is autistic, there is no me, only it, we are the same, me and it?

However you say it, the interpretation is blurred. I find reaching for equivalents helps me understand what things may mean.

I can say I am English quite happily. I would not expect anyone to equate that with my whole personality. I would

91

expect them to meet me as a person and expect to find certain aspects of Englishness about me. But when they discovered I am not a big tea drinker it would not be that much of a shock to them and it would not make them think I am not English.

In the same way, I am autistic. Meet me, as a person, expect autistic traits, but do not be surprised if they are not all there. When I say "I am autistic", I am not declaring my identity, just my belonging to a group of people who share common ground with me, not through merit, or decision, but through she[e]r chance of birth.

10.6 Hiding in the closet

There is a test called The Sally Anne Test used to see if children have developed theory of mind: the ability to put oneself into another's shoes. In the test, Sally places a marble in her basket and leaves the room. When she is gone, Anne removes the marble from Sally's basket and places it elsewhere.

Test participants are asked where Sally will look for the marble when she returns. Those with theory of mind will say the basket, understanding that Sally does not know the marble was moved. Those who have not developed theory of mind will point to where Anne put the marble, not realising that Sally could not know that it was moved.

Part of my diagnosis is underdeveloped theory of mind. People with Asperger's tend to pass the Sally Anne Test, but they do it by relying on their logic rather than whatever it is other people rely on to do it.

I believed I would pass the test, but I am in my thirties so of course I would.

This week I realised it is not so simple. Of course, I would pass that test, because I have seen it, I have read about it, I know the answer. But that test plays itself out over and over again through life and I do not always spot when it is happening.

This week my partner said in passing that we would have to transfer some money to cover a bill. The bill was going to be paid from my account, where I had more than enough money to cover it in my current account and savings account, so I assumed the bill was much higher than we had been expecting as it was going to need us to transfer money.

Later that evening I asked when they were transferring the money. My partner looked a little put out and said they thought I was doing it. I said, "I thought you were doing it," to which they grudgingly replied that they would do it now.

Then I realised. We were living the Sally Anne Test. I had assumed they knew how much money I had; because I had that knowledge, I assumed they had it. I tried to back track, but the money had already been transferred.

It sounds like a gentle misunderstanding. But I thought I was understanding the world and now lots of gentle slips like this are being revealed to me and it has had quite a disabling effect.

The more aware I become of the way I am misunderstanding the world, the less I can trust my own thoughts to guide me through it and the more frightened I become moving around in it.

So this week I did not.

This week I curled up on one corner of the sofa. I drew the curtain so neighbours could not see me and the lights were not too bright.

In my dreams I dreamt of people coming to get me, of needing to build a barricade, to shutter the windows, brace the door. Leave my job, get a quieter one, one where I am not seen, not known.

I do not feel safe.

10.7 Even 'out' it is still locked inside

My partner was listening to me struggling to explain my diagnosis to my sister on a Skype call. "I find some social situations difficult," I said. "So do I," came the reply. "Me too," came his echo from behind me.

After the call I was put out. "Don't you think it is real?" I asked. "Because it is. I can't explain it, but it is different and if you think it is just the same you are not recognising all the effort I go to in order to make it seem that way."

"It is not that, it is just that you are not *telling* her the differences."

He is right: I am not.

I am explaining myself in predictable obvious ways. Even here.

Why?

Well, because I cannot explain the other stuff. I cannot see it myself. I may try to step out of the closet but those insights are still locked inside.

I had a job once, working with young people with autism. I was good at it. Turns out people with autism do have theory of mind, it is just that it is for other people with autism. It stands to reason!

As I did that job, my colleagues would often talk about their own autistic traits and joke about them. "Oh, we are all on the spectrum here" was a common refrain. And not one I want to disagree with. I imagine the spread of autistic tendencies through the population is a pretty standard bell curve. But this attitude did not help me and did not help the young people we were supporting.

I first suspected I had autism when I was around eleven years old. I thought I had learnt to be normal, and so when I was still struggling with the social world in my late twenties, I just assumed everyone was. And when the people around me said they were autistic too then I felt a pressure to disregard, or not value, my own autistic traits. Everyone was struggling, so if I was finding it any harder that was down to my own failings, not to any autistic tendencies.

It did not help the young people we were supporting as it fostered a false impression of sameness. Not all staff, but some, took it too far. They considered themselves the same as the young people we supported just because they

94

preferred a particular brand of coffee or did not like to wear seamed socks. And once established in their hearts that they were the same, then there was no justification in their minds for the young person to be screaming with fear, or violently trying to escape a situation, that they themselves could tolerate. They viewed those children as naughty, or in need of discipline, not as autistic and experiencing the world differently.

When I went to the doctors with a list of my failings, it was a list of these silly autistic traits which I have by the handful. But these things are not my disability.

I cannot write and tell you about my disability because it is invisible to me. I know it is there. It is very, very real. When I am in the middle of a conversation that is growing ever more fraught and I have no idea why, and when I get told off for my incorrect body language or I have it pointed out that my words could not have meant any-thing other than something terrible and cruel, and I cannot claw my way back and I do not understand any of it, and I cannot, I physically cannot, it is like something just is not there in my head: Then I know it is real, but I do not know what *it* is.

(My experiences echo those reported by Jeremey in pop out box 22: 'I think being autistic is challenging my relationship'.)

When I was eight years old, I read Douglas Adam[s]'s [The] Hitchhiker's Guide to the Galaxy.[92] In it there is a character in there called Zaphod who discovers a part of his own brain has been hidden from him, by himself. When I read it, I found the notion of this hidden brain fascinating. It is a story I have come back to in my mind over and over again, worrying at it and not knowing why. From time to time, I have tried and failed to use it to explain myself to a partner or a friend. "It is like there's a hole in my mind," I would say only to be met with a puzzled look, a raised eyebrow and the typical 'Yes anyway' shrug that people use when I say something left of field. Post diagnosis I know what is in that hidden part of my brain. It is autism.

10.8 I am not right anymore

I was told off by someone I respect for "using your autism card".

She said I should still try to speak to people on the phone, and not ask the world to adapt to me.

Is she right?

Binary thinking is part of my diagnosis. But ... maybe this is not a binary thing, can I use it sometimes, for some people, and not others?

I have fallen silent at home. I walk around the house. I used to be right.

It is wrong to put a bin down in front of where the drawers open.

It is wrong to put a letter to one side and wait to deal with it later.

It is wrong to leave the organic waste piling high on the counter.

It is wrong to forget the cloth at dinner time.

I was right about all of these things. Now every time I think of one of them, I think how objectionable and sharp they sound.

I had thought everything out, sorted it all into right and wrong. There is a right way to put a knife on the draining board and a wrong one. I knew which was which, I was righteous and right, and clear of thought. Now it is wrong to be right, and I can see it really clearly.

That list is a small one and already I sound horrible.

I did not mean to be horrible, I was just trying to get things right.

Now I am silent.

11 Reflecting on the impact of diagnosis on my identity

This chapter reflects on how being diagnosed as autistic initially robbed me of the sense of identity I had prior to being diagnosed. It explores how an aspect of autism often pathologised – that of repetitive focus on a single item – can hold hidden meaning, and how for me this meaning was tied to my burgeoning sense of identity. This leads us to consider how the pathologising of autism affects and effects the wider experience of autism and autistic identity.

11.1 Identity erased

Reading back through the old blog posts in Chapter 10 now makes me wonder how much more I actually understand today than I did then. Have I any more answers or am I simply able to phrase the things I do not understand more clearly?

What is noticeable to me as I thumb through the pages of this personal history is how my very first experience of telling someone I was autistic was also my first experience of having to defend that statement (10.1). I notice that in my writing I immediately pick up the blame for the misunderstandings in my relationship, Jeremey's experience (pop out box 22: 'I think being autistic is challenging my relationship') has been similar. Milton's research (pop out box 19: 'Double empathy research') further confirms that autistic people tend to shoulder the blame for misunderstandings within relationships.

Taking the blame, or taking responsibility, was not something I did well within the relationship itself: I would always argue that I was right with my partner, and yet in my writing at the same time I placed myself as wholly culpable. Was that because I was being told it was my fault? Was it because I was wrong but was too proud to admit it? Was it because the process of diagnosis by deficit taught me that to be autistic was to have something wrong with you? After all no one sends you to get diagnosed because you are being brilliant, do they?

As the posts chart days further from diagnosis I can see in them my identity starting to fade; at first it is a relief that the problems are not all my own doing, but then the diagnosis takes away my abilities. Things I would have identified myself as being were no longer me, they were autism. What was I?

At the end of section 10.5, I state that when I say I am autistic I am *not* declaring my identity. A statement I was surprised to read. My argument as to why this is at the time stands to reason, but I think the subsequent slide into feeling disabled and losing confidence in myself are connected. All through the posts I waver between person-first and condition-first language, and between looking for signs of disability and looking for signs of difference.

Prior to diagnosis, I considered myself to be defined by a number of things. Number one on this list of self-definition was a sense of being different to others. After that there were a multitude of what I would have considered to be faults and a handful of strengths with loyalty, moral conduct and work ethic or concentration coming top of the list.

In one hit, at diagnosis I lost all of the things I defined myself against. None of them were me anymore. I was not different. I was autistic, and in being autistic I was the same in a lot of ways as a lot of other people. The faults were not mine to own, and neither were the strengths. My *self* had vanished, and without that defining sense of self, I began to crumble.

I did not see autistic as an identity, one that would scoop up all those lost things and give them back to me.

In contrast to those early post-identification days (Chapter 10) is this piece (11.2), which I wrote four years after diagnosis:

11.2 *Say Yes to the Dress*

I watch the television series *Say Yes to the Dress*.[93] If you have not had the pleasure of seeing it, here is what happens: a potential bride comes into the store, and says she wants an original dress. She wants to look different and unique because she is not like other brides. She then tries on a range of white dresses, which all exist in a shop (a shop that all the other brides shop in) before buying a white dress.

The same thing happens several times in every single episode. My husband thought I might stop watching the programme after we got married, but my interest in it was never anything to do with the dresses. I find its simplicity and repetition wonderfully relaxing.

I have always identified myself as different, and been identified as such.

I know everyone thinks of themselves as unique (the brides tell me this each episode) and I know that everyone *is* unique. But not everyone has that all-permeating sense of otherness.

I have been called weird by bullies, and fondly by friends who like their weirdo. When I wrote my application for college, I did not write the usual things. I wrote a polemic about how I was different, ending it with the startling line: "I am not a sheep!"

I doubt the college got many other applications that year that so strongly declared their lack of Ovis aries tendencies. When I got my first teaching post, I was called to interview off the back of a similarly standout letter which ended in the bold declaration: "I believe pity erodes life."

A statement I also used to front my Beyond Boarders TEDx talk: 'Inclusion: For Pity's Sake?'[94]

I have always *felt* different. The feeling is not a defiant one, it is more of a suspicion. A sense that deep down I was different. I had no 'like-you' experiences to base relationships upon.

And then I got diagnosed as autistic. It turns out I really was different. I have a different type of brain. It makes sense of why my responses were never the same as those of my peers.

Being diagnosed has flipped the difference that I feel entirely. I read things written by other autistics and wonder if I wrote them and just forgot about them. I have my own personal problems and it turns out they are identikit problems to other women on the spectrum.

I am not different, I am a cookie-cutter version of a particular type of person.

I mean, of course, I am still different, and unique and so on, but now that level of difference is about the same as the brides on the show.

When one comes on who says, "I want a dress that is just like every other bride's," that is when we will have found the truly unique one!

11.2.1 Repeated study

When I develop fascinations for things there is usually a reason behind them, as with Zaphod in *The Hitchhiker's Guide to the Galaxy* (10.7) and Jem's[95] song 'Just a Ride' which crops up in section 13.4. Incidentally as I wrote this book, I had two lines of a song[96] caught in my head as an earworm. A very unusual occurrence for me as I do not listen to music. I did not pay them much attention, other than to presume they indicated a wish to be wiser or for lockdown[1] to be over. It was only as I finished the book that I realised why they had become lodged in my head.[2]

The repetition and predictability of *Say Yes to the Dress* was relaxing, but its continuing grip on me had more to do with my brain toying with ideas of individuality and identity than in a desire to unwind.

In the blog posts in Chapter 10, I am lost without the sense of self I had been used to. But in the *Say Yes to the Dress* piece (11.2), written more than three years later, I sound happier to be one of a crowd. It is understandable that it would take someone used to operating alone a while to come around to the idea of being a part of a group.

The capacity of an autistic mind to focus on a topic and study it repeatedly is one first observed by Asperger[97] who used "little professors" as a term of endearment to describe the hundreds of autistic children he studied. This capacity can be observed in people from all parts of the spectrum. Asperger respected it and sought to understand the topics his little professors were studying. Kanner,[98] after studying only a few autistic children, pathologised it, dismissing the repetitive actions of the children he saw as meaningless.

It is interesting to consider where respect for difference could lead us as we support those for whom the experience of being autistic overlaps with one of being disabled. Particularly interesting for someone like me who lives on a part of the autistic spectrum "systematically excluded"[36] (p. 380) by Kanner from his original diagnostic category of autism.

15

The Shoeness of a Shoe

An extract from Elly Chapple's TEDx talk – 'Diversity is the key to our survival: the Shoeness of a Shoe'[99]

TW

Elly's TEDx talk begins with a harrowing account of how her daughter Ella became deaf and blind as a result of injuries she sustained whilst physically expressing her frustration with how she was being taught. Part way through her talk, Elly gives an account of Ella studying their family's shoes:

We have a crate at our front door, it's nothing fancy, I have a husband and three kids, I don't have time to display my shoes like a Pinterest board. And every day for nine months my daughter would sit and go through this crate twice a day. At first people thought this was cute or interesting. Around three months I could see they were all becoming slightly awkward about it, and at six months some of the more official visitors said to me that this was obsessive and I needed to stop her.

> And I said, but I haven't figured out what she is doing yet: Have you?
>
> And I decided we were going to listen to Ella this time. And it was really hard just to observe and be humble and open to the clues that she gave. It was really hard not to steer her. And one day after nine months she stood up and she walked across the hallway and she sat down on the chair and she stuck her foot out and said, "boots".
>
> She'd learned everything she'd needed to learn and she was done. And she never did it again. And I got it, this time I got it. Ella was showing us her world. This is how *I* learn, this is how *I* do things, this is *me*, and *I* can do it.
>
> And I mentally drew a line in the sand, because I realised once you took the stressful environment away, and the people who didn't believe, and you treated her like a human being, she could achieve like anyone.
>
> I decided I would no longer allow my daughter to be forced to learn in a way that she couldn't. This time we were going to listen to her. We were going to connect with Ella. We were going to work with her, not do to her, and in doing so widen our view. And the assumptions from the past faded away. And I realised that although Ella had lost her sight, she had given us great vision and the shoeness of a shoe was complete.

11.3 Deficit and pathology

Finding a sense of identity at the end of a pathway laid out according to deficit and pathology is a hard thing to do. When neurological difference is automatically presumed to indicate deficit, it is easy for people to conclude that the challenges thrown up by this difference are best fixed by amending the perceived deficit. In other

16

What does the Shoeness of a Shoe really teach us?

Elly Chapple, founder of CanDoElla https://candoella. com and the #Flipthenarrative campaign

When my daughter really opened my eyes to what it means to really listen, I realised your eyes and ears only tell you so much. Considering that 95% or there-abouts of our learning comes from these two senses, what is the world like when these are deprived? It is one thing to read about the impact or study it, and another to live and walk it. The real understanding comes from our willingness to walk with someone to see the world in the way they do. The mantra often discussed in the deafblind world is one that works for many – doing with someone, not to or for.

Is it that simple? To start the journey, yes. Engaging at the point of where someone is, and working with them to understand that point of view, is key to our own world opening much further. Ella taught us that to learn through her primary sense of touch took far longer than our speedy auditory or visual pathways. What we can delineate in seconds with our eyes or ears can take far longer when your hands are your eyes. Again, it sounds simple, but if we usually rely heavily on our primary senses of vision and hearing, it can take us a lot longer to accommodate the time needed for learning through touch. It requires that we remain present, in the moment, to understand what the focus is, and the process by which an object or a space or an experience becomes an understood 'thing'. The next step is about what that represents emotion-ally – and conceptually. I can hear our teacher in my head often reminding us that our concept of the world is far removed often from that of someone who is working primarily with touch, but also residual hearing and some light/dark perception.

Knowledge of the person is critical within the learning space because the relationship is key to seeing beyond things we may assume or dismiss. Often it can feel uncomfortable to work outside of knowns or parameters set for learning, but often it can lead us to much greater understanding and a different way of seeing the world. The trust we need to form within the relationships is key, for both parties to lean in and work together. That in itself presents us with a mindset shift, that everyone can learn, albeit differently, and that the value in that difference is key to us broadening our own ways of developing and understanding, to be able to grow as human beings working with one another in a world full of difference, that is both profoundly beautiful and insightful. The world is rapidly becoming a space with more and more difference, perhaps it was always there, but we can see more clearly now. It asks that we grow ourselves, by spending more time working with people we can learn from – while also learning together. A sharing of knowledge from differing points of view of the world that can only further enhance our whole space to be and truly begin to flip the narrative around our own concepts of why and how.

words, the responsibility to change, in order to avoid future difficulties, is placed firmly on the shoulders of the person who is considered to be 'other' to the established norm.

Functioning under the weight of other people's expectations that you should change, or your own sense of being responsible for those changes, is difficult. Quite naturally the challenge of carrying this weight of expectation and responsibility leads to secondary problems like low self-esteem, anxiety, and a loss of confidence, which in turn will have an effect on other areas of life.

We could look at the increased risk of mental ill health associated with being autistic and conclude that autistic brains cope less well with life. But were those burdens shared out more evenly, perhaps the statistics would speak otherwise of our apparent deficits.

17

Autism and mental health

TW

Numerous studies point out the increased risk of mental illness associated with being autistic.[51,60,100-110] A large UK-based study[111] of the experiences of autistic adults and their families reported that at least a third of autistic adults have serious mental health problems.

Autistics are more likely to self-harm than neurotypicals[112-117] and are more likely to die by or attempt suicide.[112,118-130,197-199] Autistic vulnerability to suicide is explored further in pop out box 27: 'Suicide risk factors'.

Autism is not a mental illness. Experiences associated with not being understood, and not having access to the same support as other people, feed into the increased risk of mental ill health experienced by autistics.[101,104,131-133] For example, researchers[100] note that autistic people have increased risks of negative life experiences (something explored in pop out box 24: 'Health inequalities and more') and that these should be considered as causal factors in the increased rates of mental ill health observed in autistic adults.

Experiences, such as those described by Jayne in pop out box 13: 'Defending the reality of a condition', of not being believed, or not being understood, (e.g. pop out box 22: 'Jeremey: I think being autistic is challenging my relationship') place additional stress on individuals' mental health. In contrast, some research[51] has indicated that claiming an autistic identity can have a protective effect with regard to mental health.

In addition to the increased vulnerability to mental ill health incurred through negative life experiences, prejudice, misunderstanding and misdiagnosis, autistic people face a further threat to their wellbeing from scientific ignorance. Research into mental health often purposefully excludes autistic people,[112] meaning that new knowledge is based on neuro-normative assumptions. We know that autistic people express themselves differently to neurotypical people.[105] Models for identifying and supporting people who are experiencing mental ill health based solely on neurotypical people offer support only to neurotypical people.

There may also be funding biases at play when it comes to acquiring knowledge that could support autistic people's mental health. I was personally dismayed when a search of Google Scholar to inform the writing of this section, using the search terms 'Autistic' and 'Mental Health', did not yield any results about the mental health of autistic people for a considerable number of pages. Instead, the primary results focused on the mental health of parents of autistics, which of course is worthy of study, but one could not help wondering whether having made more inroads into supporting the mental health of their children might have had a positive knock-on effect on the mental health of parents; after all, there are few parents whose mental health is improved by witnessing their children suffer.

The blog posts in Chapter 10 detail the beginnings of what was later to become a total breakdown in communication between my partner and myself. Is such a breakdown inevitable across a neurological divide?

Imagine a language similar to your mother tongue, but in which words you use to denote certain items or actions have subtly different meanings. As you speak to someone who uses this language, you will both believe you are speaking a common tongue. Misunderstandings will occur.

Whose fault are the misunderstandings?

How would you decide?

Would fault be apportioned based on the number of native speakers?

Would you seek out a dictionary in which it was possible to identify the correct meaning of words from the incorrect meaning? Who would write such a dictionary?

Suppose, in this imagined scenario, that someone discovers that there are two languages, when before people on both sides of the divide presumed there to be only one.

Whose fault are the misunderstandings now?

At whose feet lies the mammoth task of translation?

We could argue about the proportional split of the translation responsibility from one side to the other (presumably those more capable of doing the translation should be allocated the task), but I think we will agree that both sides hold a share of that responsibility. Researchers[135] note that autistic people are disproportionately held accountable for breakdowns in understanding within relationships.

In the pathologising of autism, autistics have been accused of being unable to cross the divide created by different neurological blueprints. Some researchers[136] suggest, however, that autistics might actually be better than neurotypicals at crossing the divide, not because we have greater skills but simply because there has been demand on us to cross the divide in order to function in life. If the accusations are true and our brains are less flexible than the brains of neurotypicals, then there is a clear argument to say that the effort of translation ought to fall on the more capable shoulders.

Incidentally, unbeknownst to me when I wrote the analogy above about subtly different languages, this has actually been a topic of study. Researchers[137] noted that the phrasing and interpreting of language can have an effect on how it is understood by autistics and non-autistics; it is as if there is an autistic language and a non- autistic language that subtly overlap and confuse speakers on both sides. In relation to this, Milton[138] (n.p.) comments: "even in quite subtle ways, words and uses in context can mean quite different things for people with different dispositions and perspectives".

18

A glimpse of the future in *Gnomon*, based on Harkaway[139]

Nick Harkaway's sci-fi book *Gnomon* (p. 31) gives a glimpse of a near future in which an understanding of neurodiversity is more commonplace:

Hinde wears a badge with a rainbow on it. A few decades ago this would have meant something about her sexual orientation, but now it's a polite signal to Neith and anyone else Hinde interacts with that she is not neurotypical. Her brain touches a particular peak of the modern medical taxonomy that includes some autisms and various perceptual and processing functions such as synaesthesia, and structural (rather than acquired) hypervigilance. It is not actually a spectrum in the linear sense, more a graph on several axes.

The badge acts as an external signal of neurodivergence and so, when later in the text a misunderstanding occurs because a neurotypical person asks an indirect question, the neurotypical person feels embarrassed by their social faux pas and immediately alters the phrasing of their question to better suit the neurodivergent person they are talking to. It is a glimpse of an imagined world where the weight of responsibility for translating across the neuro divide appears equally weighted:

"And no le[si]ons?"
"No."
"A medical error," Neith supposes.
Hinde doesn't respond straight away because this is only implicitly a question. Her face takes on an uncomfortable look as she tries to work out how to respond. Neith, embarrassed to approximately the same degree that she would be if she had loudly broken wind, changes her wording.
"Was it an accident? Malpractice?"

19

Double empathy research

"The claim that autistic people lack a Theory of Mind pervades psychology", yet it is "empirically question-able and societally harmful".[140] (p. 102)

Damian Milton has reinterpreted old conceptions of theory of mind into the double empathy problem, highlighting that perspective taking and empathy are both two-way processes.[136] Milton (n.D.) explains: "It is a 'double problem' as both people experience it, and so it is not a singular problem located in any one person." He goes on to note that until very recently, research has "ignored the difficulties that non autistic people have in understanding autistic perspectives".[136] Studies[135,141–143] that have looked at the interaction processes between autistics and non-autistics add weight to Milton's reframing of this problem as a two-way process, finding that misunderstandings occur on both sides of the neurological divide.

Milton[144] brings our attention to how our starting point for questions about autism and neurodiversity can bias the conclusions we draw. He explains that framing autism within cognitive neuroscience or psychology leads to a particular understanding of autism, often one that is deficit-based. Conversations about autism that begin in cognitive or behavioural differences focus on the autistic person and their presumed deficits. Such conversations do not look at how we all relate and interact with each other, and yet relating to and interacting with each other is how society is formed.

Society is made by the people who, quite literally, *make* it up. It is a constructed entity of shared understanding between people, rather than a predefined framework. When autistic people are included in the creation of society from the start, the making of society can take place in an inclusive fashion. When neurodivergent people are included in research[41,145–146] and are presumed to be equals, not inferiors, the problems and deficits associated with autism, by conversations that start outside of a relational perspective, show up clearly as being present on both sides.

Understanding society and relationships to be created things, rather than pre-existing templates we must all adhere to, helps us to see the two-wayness of these misunderstandings. Milton[144] (p. 884) gives the example of "The inability to 'read' the subtext of a social situation" as often being "deemed to be a major feature of those diagnosed as being on the autism spectrum". This much-cited deficit presumes there is a subtext which is in some way predetermined. But of course, that is not true; in any interaction, the subtext is co-created by those involved.

If we view interactions, understanding, relationships, society, empathy and so on as shared processes of construction, then it is clear that the inability to read people across the neurological divide exists on both sides of that divide. As Milton[144] (p. 884) puts it: "The 'theory of mind' and 'empathy' so lauded in normative psychological models of human interaction refers to the ability a 'non-autistic spectrum' (non-AS) individual has to assume understandings of the mental states and motives of other people." In other words, people are celebrated as being empathetic and as having theory of mind, based on their assumption that other people think and feel as they do. When autistic people make these same assumptions, they are condemned as not having empathy or theory of mind and are pathologised for doing so. Milton[144] (p. 884) observes that: "The 'empathy' problem being a 'two-way street' has been mentioned by both 'autistic writers'[147] and non-AS writers[148] alike and yet, despite such protestations, the 'lack of theory of mind' myth persists."

To hear Milton and other researchers discussing double empathy, readers might be interested to listen to the Dr Brett Double Empathy Series.[149]

11.4 Coming out

Beginning to identify myself using the word autistic was a strange experience for me. It had the feeling of running across stepping stones without knowing which would hold my weight and which would tip me into cold water.

I have been a supporter of LGBTQ+ rights ever since I knew what homosexuality meant. I remember as a child being baffled by the idea that anyone could think two adults loving each other was wrong based on what was between their legs or what clothes they chose to wear. As I began telling more people, "I am autistic", I found myself thinking about the many 'coming out' narratives I have heard through the years and drawing parallels between them and my own experience of 'coming out' as autistic.

I drew these parallels tentatively, very aware that the experiences of the two communities have been markedly different. LGBTQ+ people have been taught to feel shame for who they are, their love has been judged to be morally wrong. Whereas autistics have been treated as defective and judged to be intellectually inferior. Both have been, and in some parts of the world continue to be, subjected to horrific 'cure' treatments, but there is nowhere in the world where it is illegal to be autistic, nor has autism ever been considered a lifestyle choice.

Eugenics programmes such as the Nazis' Aktion T4 saw autistics murdered, and incidents of filicide of autistic people are all too regularly reported on the news.[150] [3] LGBTQ+ people were similarly targeted by Nazi eugenics programmes, they have been and remain the victims of filicide. In addition to this awful shared experience stands a notable distinction: at the time of writing, 12 countries in the world still hold penal laws which state that homosexuality should be punishable by death.[151] Nowhere in the world has laws which suggest that autistic people should be put to death. There are similarities between the prejudice experienced by each community, but the experience has not been the same.

In a society that understood sexual and neurological diversity there would be no need for anyone to officially 'come out' as there would be no assumption of a common norm.

In pop out box 2 part 1: 'Jeremey: I think I am autistic but I do not want to be diagnosed', Jeremey reflects on how his negative experiences of coming out as gay influence his decision not to seek a diagnosis of autism. Rachel's experiences have been different; here she draws a comparison between her experiences of coming out as gay and coming out as autistic:

20

Coming out experiences

Rachel Barker, lead practitioner in an area special needs school, MEd student in SPMLD, golf enthusiast and wakeboarder

People often ask me when I came out. Sometimes I respond with the obligatory coming out story, but the truest reply I could give would be to ask them: "Which time?"

Despite leaps forward in acceptance of different sexualities and genders, and a better understanding of neurodivergence, society's subconscious bias will always assume you are straight and neurotypical.

When I was first diagnosed as autistic, I explained to a friend that it felt like coming out all over again. Her reply surprised me: "Which is harder?" she queried. An answer still eludes me. What I do know is that the responses remain the same each time I come out:

"You don't look gay/autistic!"

"Being gay/autistic doesn't really affect you that much, does it?"

What people generally mean by the first is that I do not fit their perception of a gay or autistic person.

It is an odd conundrum. Does not fitting in the boxes in their heads somehow invalidate me?

Am I not doing gay right?

Am I not doing autistic right?

I know logically that these questions are irrational, but their comments put me on the defensive. Rightly or wrongly, they make me feel judged. And, they entirely miss the point: being gay and being autistic are crucial parts of my identity. They are as much a part of me being me, as being right-handed is (incidentally, I never get told that I must actually be left-handed).

Questioning their existence is akin to saying, "Are you sure you got you right?"

To some extent being gay is more obvious: anyone meeting my partner would presume my sexuality. However, that does not mean people naturally assume this without the visual or verbal cues. For me this is where the parallel with being autistic becomes really clear. Despite the late diagnosis, my autism has always been noticeable. It was there in the pulling of my sleeves over my hands, in the biting of my clothes and nails, in the constant fidgeting. It was there in the reluctance to miss a sports practice and in my interruptions of teachers. It was there. My classmates noticed I was different even if they did not have the words to describe how. They made sure that I knew too.

The simplest answer to the second question is yes. Yes, it does affect me. All the time. Sometimes less and sometimes more, but the answer is always, yes. Because I am in the fortunate position to be able to verbalise how I am affected, this often has the surprising effect of people assuming that it is a subject up for debate. To be clear, my identity is not up for debate. I would not expect anyone to justify their identity or defend the difficulties they experience. I am happy to talk about my identity; I just do not expect it to be challenged.

12 Blog part two: the first months after diagnosis

Part two of my blog covers the second and third month post-diagnosis. In it I constantly question myself and the way I see the world. I become particularly aware of my thought processes and my masking. The masking and the diminishment of my sense of self through perpetual double thinking are examined more closely below before the blog posts start. In addition to those concerns, in this part of the blog you will witness me continuing to pathologise anything I recognise as being autistic within my life.

12.1 Give up masking?

In section two of my blog, you can eavesdrop on some of the tensions that not having a shared language within my relationship at the time caused. When I was writing these posts, I often wished I appeared 'more' autistic. I reasoned that if my differences were more obvious, the need for translation would be more apparent as a shared responsibility.

From time to time, members of the online autistic community would encourage me to give up masking, as if masking were its literal interpretation: a mask held up to one's face, and I could simply put it down. Masking as a skill, rather than as a piece of costumery, is a very hard thing to give up. The gallery thought experiment illustrates why the skill of masking is a difficult thing to surrender: Imagine you are in a gallery space, exploring a piece of installation art. Ropes are tied at ankle and shin height in a random crisscross pattern covering the floor space. You are blindfolded.

115

As you try to move within this environment it is likely that at first you will trip, stumble, fall, and get tangled in the ropes. Unbeknownst to you, no one else in the space is blindfolded. They all move around with relative ease, discussing the pictures on the walls and what they ate for dinner or what they plan to do next. Conversations which are entirely irrelevant to you. You want to talk about the ropes: about where they are, how tightly they are tied, the reasons for the patterns you are beginning to suspect are there.

Now suppose you lived in that room for years. Occasionally someone might mention something about where the ropes are, but in the main you learn through personal experience where they are. Gradually you begin to be able to move clumsily about the place. Eventually after years of study you are as nimble as a ballerina.

You are pleased with your skills, proud of your hard-won agility. Occasionally you still get snared in a rope, and sometimes new ropes are added or old ropes are moved and these catch you out. But the other people in the room also get twisted and knotted up from time to time when they are not paying attention to their foot-fall. At times, your movements may even appear more graceful than theirs because you have honed them so precisely whereas theirs are carried out practically. You dance amongst the ropes and your fellow gallery goers.

One day you learn that you are blindfolded and the other people are not. The other people in the gallery learn this too. Your blind-fold cannot be removed, but you are told to walk as yourself. The other people say you no longer need to leap about so delicately. If you get tangled up, they will understand.

Would you stop dancing?

Would it be less effort to go back to blundering about the place and getting into tangles? Yes, you would save the energy that you expend in executing your careful leaps, but you might use it up again untangling the knots.

Would you take off the mask?

The idea that autistics like me who have spent years mastering the art of masking (I am not at ballerina level by a long way yet) would instantly want, or find it easy, to stop masking is naïve. Stopping leaping does not take the ropes or the blindfold away.

The effort involved in masking takes energy, but over time we build up a certain stamina (a not unending one) so that it seems easier.

12.2 Double thinking diminishes me

Another thing evident in section two of my blog, which was written several months after diagnosis, is the impact of my brain's capacity to focus intently on a topic. This focus can be incredibly constructive, but equally as destructive.

Through this time, I was hyper aware of the need to think everything twice: was that thought valid or was that thought autistic and in some way invalidated by being so? My brain latched onto the notion of my binary thinking as being wrong. An odd meta level of binary thinking which I did not appreciate at the time emerged as I thought about whether my thoughts about things being right or wrong were themselves either right or wrong.

My focus on how important the rightness and wrongness of small tasks were to me actively undermined my self-esteem and sense of self. As a result of this I began acting in harmful ways.

By the time I was writing the blog posts below, the blog itself had gathered a few followers. Their comments were often compassionate and supportive, they led me to explore further the online world of being autistic.

Social media rarely presents people at their best and I feared that I was looking, not so much in at the autistic world through the window of my computer screen, but at myself again in a mirror. Was I really like the angry online keyboard warriors I encountered on Twitter and Facebook?

It is worth asking why I identified the keyboard warriors as representative of autism, but did not do the same for the kind commenters on my blog.

12.3 Blog part two

This section of the blog begins with me considering my binary thinking; this is a theme that continues throughout the blog. (For another perspective on the black and white thinking of autistics, see Eartharcher.[152])

12.3.1 Is my binary thinking right or wrong?

Binary thinking: the tendency to view things as either right or wrong, is a part of my diagnosis.

As you read this you will probably try to decide whether I am right or wrong:

He was on his way to put the bins out, but got distracted.

I moved to take the bins out instead. I was aware that earlier in the day I had dropped a half empty tin of tomatoes into the bin, so I was not planning on tipping it.

He said, in what I heard to be a slightly stroppy voice: "it is wet at the bottom."

I said: "that doesn't mean I can't take the bin out."

He said: "there's no need to be aggressive."

Although I could probably repeat the rest of it verbatim that is all of it, three sentences and it was over.

Of course, it is my blog, so I will say I was not being aggressive, but it is clear there are other responses like "thanks for letting me know" or "yes I know, I dropped a wet thing earlier."

I have learned to apologise. I apologise whenever he is offended or angry. He apologises too. We are both sorry we cannot communicate.

But communication is two way, it is co-constructed. If he believed I am kind he would hear my mis-phrased communications as the mistakes that they are. If he believes I am cruel he will hear my mis-phrased communications as confirmation of that cruelty. If I was better at responding I would not say the things that get us into this mess. If I was better at discerning his feelings, I would not think he is angry when he is not.

We have been together for years.

What is the future?

I cannot predict when he will find me offensive. If I were doing it with intent then I could try not to do it. Would I be able to predict it if I wasn't autistic? Or, if I wasn't autistic would I not say offensive things? If I want to avoid him being cross with me all I can do is try not to do anything. Do not speak. Walk on eggshells. He feels the same.

He has every right to be offended when I say something offensive.

If he understood me, he would not feel offended, he could help me to say the right thing or point simply point out that I have made a mistake. What am I not understanding about him?

If I just blanket apologise for everything he declares to be wrong then he is in charge of what is right and what is wrong.

What if sometimes he *is* wrong to be offended?

Apparently understanding things in this binary way is a part of the condition. It certainly feels disabling now.

12.3.2 So cross I could cry

TW

As a child I used to annoy my sister by calling her a baby. If an adult came near, I would change my tone so that it sounded affectionate. My sister did not want to be called a baby. My continuance at doing it would drive her to ever greater heights of frustration until she would be angry, crying, and attempting what violence she knew as a five year old.

You can probably relate to a time in your life when you were so frustrated by a small thing, and your own powerlessness, that you could cry. Probably knowing that it was a small thing did not help. If anything, it makes it worse. It makes it all the more humiliating.

This is how I feel when I am at home. I do not know what happens. I do not know why home is different, but it is. The minute I leave the house I feel the stress lift. I look back on the people in the house and feel nothing but affection and compassion for them (compassion that they have to live with me).

A few months ago in desperation I slashed my forearm with a bread knife to make a point, and it worked. I did not do it with any intent. We were in the kitchen, I could not explain, I quite literally grabbed for it as a way of showing feeling instead of speaking feeling. Somehow that, as an act of communication, expressed what I meant better than my words and my tears.

What am I angry about?

That the recycling was left on the side...

That a book was not put away...

That something I put somewhere was moved...

That a sentence was said wrong...

That too much food was put on my plate...

Seriously?

I am a grown up. I know none of these things warrant the response I give them.

What am I angry about?

I am angry that I mind.

I am angry at myself.

I am angry at my own small mindedness.

Most of all I am angry at him for showing it to me, because it is only there when he is there. Without a witness these things get done, the sentences get said as I would say them, the physical objects in the house are where I put them.

What can I do?

Well, practically speaking, a glass of wine in the afternoon means I mind less. Minding less has the knock-on effect of me being happier about myself, because I dislike the me who minds so much. In minding less there instantly becomes less to mind about.

I recognise that I am self-medicating with alcohol. I think I have the dose right.

12.3.3 *Worn out by wearing so many layers*

TW

I am exhausted.

The mental effort of checking if what I think or what I say, is 'right' or if what I think or what I say is merely a result of a quirk of the wiring of my brain, and therefore deserving of being checked, is wearing me out.

I have to think about everything twice, and I already thought about things really carefully before I was diagnosed.

I do not feel mentally unwell. I do not want to kill myself. But I do feel as if I have, quite literally, run out of energy.

There is no stopping checking because you cannot un-know things (maybe I should be wishing for a swift blow to the head?) There is no rest. I know there is a layer outside of my own mind now, so I have to check whether I correlate with it or not.

Pandora's box is open and I cannot shut it.

12.3.4 *Absence makes the heart grow fonder*

The house is quiet. Clock ticking. There is a photo of me and my small family on the wall in front of me.

I feel a burgeoning sense of calm.

Ironically this is exciting: Perhaps it will stay? Perhaps it will sink in? Perhaps I'll be able to think clearly?

In the photo on the wall, I stand shoulder to elbow with my partner, and he carries our newborn child. The child is sleeping. He looks happy, and I look … I am smiling but my forehead is crinkled, I look on edge, a little worried.

There is something fractious about being together in a house. Something anxiety inducing, something bordering on a gentle sense of panic. It is not overwhelming. It is like a background buzz or a static charge in the air. There is that sense of not being quite right, an idea of time running out and of not being able to stay on top of things and of … well

121

... of the bread bin not being shut and the toilet roll not being replaced and not that these things are big things, not even to me, just that they are the final straws on the back of this already very overloaded camel.

So everyone is out, and I can hear the clock ticking, and that stillness creeping in and I look at the photo and I love them, I want to be there. When they come back later, will I be able to be?

There are a lot of different places on the spectrum and nobody can, or should, judge whose life is harder. I think the word different is best. Our challenges, our struggles, are different. Trying to weigh them up in terms of less or more is a nonsense. But for me, if I were at [a] place in the spectrum where social contact truly did overwhelm, where I clearly *had* to be alone in order to survive, then my family would know about it, and if they were worth their salt it would be planned into our routines. But because I am able to manage, they get a worse version of me. They get a jagged, fractured, self-defensive, snappy me. And I do not believe that is who I am ... though who is to say ... it is who I am in this situation, but ... I do not want this to be me.

I wonder, whether if I stopped making eye contact, if I spoke a little less, holed up a little more. If I took some of the pressure off in other ways, would I get more freedom to be?

12.3.5 Sticks and stones

TW

I have no plan for what I am about to write. I do not even know if I know anything which I can write.

But my topic is bullying.

Daft as it may sound, it was another aspect of my diagnosis that surprised me.

"Have you been bullied?"

"Yes." (That is not uncommon for children, all a part of growing up etc. That that particular section of growing up lasted a few years longer than I might have liked is just the unfortunate throw of the dice combined with moving schools a few times.)

"We find a lot of adults with autism get bullied in the workplace, is this something you've experienced?"

And that is where the silence fell in my mind. I answered tentatively, "I think so?"

I had not connected these dots before myself. A lack of awareness of social norms makes it hard for me to identify when people overstep a mark. People often respond socially in ways that are not instinctual to me – how am I to know if their responses are malicious or just another example of people being different and me not understanding why?

I left a job because I could not handle interactions with my line manager on top of the pressures of the job, which were themselves very high.

I did not think of it as bullying; perhaps as a clash of personalities maybe, but mostly I just thought I was not keeping up. My understanding of bullying was playground based: adults do not do it. I doubt the person in question felt themselves to be a bully, or intended to be. They were working under the same pressure as me, if not greater because of the increased responsibility of their role compared to mine. From the very start of that job, I was predicted to be someone who would burn out, they were simply tougher than me.

A couple of incidents stand out in my mind as clearly wrong: I was shouted at in front of staff I managed. I was accused publicly of doing things I had not done. But although those moments were alarming, they were not stressful as I knew I was innocent. The more confusing moments, when I did not know if I had been wronged or not, did more damage.

I was signed off work sick. They did tests. The tests confirmed I had a serious infection. The doctor said it was due to stress. I frowned at this, went home, Googled. Found no evidence that stress causes illness, and even if it might account for some conditions how could stress cause an infection?

I told the doctor it was not stress.

I was treated with antibiotics. LOTS of antibiotics.

I took myself back to work. I had not had a day off before.

I lasted an hour before it all became too much.

I was signed off again.

I never went back.

My boss called a meeting with me and some more senior managers. They had spoken to other members of staff about what had been happening. I was informed I had a case for wrongful dismissal and could claim compensation for how my job had ended. I sought advice. It was possible that if I took the case, I would have to face my line manager in court. I walked away.

I saw them in the supermarket a few months later. I walked away then too.

Now there is a person in my life, who says they are helping me with my career, but who speaks to me in the same way that my line manager used to.

I do not know if I am paranoid or if it is happening again.

In my profession this person is well known and respected. Would they be so if they acted like this?

People have clashes of personality, how am I to know the difference between a clash in personalities and bullying?

Last night I answered them back. Not directly. Not to their face. I just put a counter opinion out there, in the public arena; the same place in which they stomp on me.

Are they stomping on me?

Is it just normal communication?

Am I taking them the wrong way?

Have I now started a fight?

How can I know?

21

Bullying

Researchers have found autistic people to be at increased risk of bullying[153-155] with some suggesting rates are three to four times higher than for neurotypical peers.[156] The National Autistic Society in the UK cited bullying as one of the primary fears of autistic children attending school.[157] In a literature review examining 17 studies, researchers found autistic children to be at greater risk of bullying/victimisation in school when compared to their neurotypical peers, estimating prevalence rates to be 44%–50%.[158] Autistic people are also more likely to be bullied by 'friends' throughout life than neurotypical people.[159]

Autistic people are at increased risk of being bullied in adulthood. In one survey,[53] 48% of autistic respondents reported experiencing bullying in the workplace. This increased prevalence is reflected in other studies and surveys.[160]

Booth[161] warns against the risks of autistics being bullied in the workplace and advises on strategies employers can use to reduce these risks. Rather strangely, other studies, carefully not cited here, recognise autistic people's increased risk of workplace bullying and go on to advise on 'therapies' autistic people could undergo in order to avoid these risks. Imagine a study that noted an increased risk of bullying for ethnic minorities in the workplace and then suggested therapies intended to make people less ethnic, or one that noted women's increased vulnerability to harassment and then suggested ways for them to seem more male. Such a study would be very unlikely to make it through the peer review process that respected journals use to ensure they publish only the best research. That victim-blaming notions can successfully navigate a route to publication intended to weed out nonsense speaks of a deeper institutionalised prejudice against autistic people.

12.3.6 Barriers between the neurotypical, the self-diagnosed neurodivergent and the professionally diagnosed neurodivergent communities

One of the things that puts me off taking part in the autistic community is the level of venom spat out by some people within it against the neurotypical world.

"Why can't NTs do this?"

"When will NTs get it?"

"NTs are so stupid they think..."

I imagine the answer to all of the above and more is because they are human. Because we are all struggling, we none of us understand things that are not in our own experience until we have had them explained to us. As humans we are limited. We may have been making a superb effort to understand people who are different to us and just not got around to a particular category yet.

Imagine if it were the other way around and a neurotypical person was saying:

"Why can't autistics do this?"

"When will autistics understand that"

"Autistics are stupid."

We would be furious.

Autistic or neurotypical, it should not matter. We know this best of all. We cannot expect a community that does not understand the need for equality of understanding to get to a position where they do understand that need any quicker just because we yelled at them.

Not only does it alienate them, it alienates autistics who do not want to be a part of bashing those neurologically different to themselves.

There is another divide: diagnosis.

I was talking to someone with a diagnosis prior to getting mine. The way they treated me pre- and post-diagnosis was totally different. Once I had my label it was as if I had passed through a magic door and was accepted.

I understand why people are so touchy about this division. It is because there are two groups of people who self-diagnose:

Those who are beginning to realise more and more that the difficulties they have in their lives line up with autism. They will, like I did, seek out people with autism to compare notes with: I feel like this, do you too?

These people should not be met with cries of, "You are not one of us until you have a label", they should be met with gentleness. They are just like us but do not have a label to protect them or to lead them to the next clue in a treasure hunt journey through understanding their own neurology.

The second group are the ones that cause the barbed wire to be added to the wall.

This group have identified with a couple of traits that link with autism: perhaps they hate it when their favourite product changes its labelling, perhaps they like to do the exact same thing every Saturday. What I notice about these people is they are often extremely socially capable. They will sit in a big group and talk about how they are "sooo autistic". I bet you can hear it in my voice now too, that little touch of venom which only at the top of this article I was preaching against (oh the irony).

Why is it there? Why am I spiky towards them? Why am I helping to put up the barbed wire?

Because their identification is not them saying, "I am the same as you, we are equal", it is them saying, "I am autistic too, so what is wrong with you is all you, you are defective."

It is them discrediting autism. I spoke to one at a party once, who eventually said about an eight-year-old boy with

127

a diagnosis that she was employed to support: "You know there's nothing wrong with that kid that the back of my hand couldn't fix."

And that is it, that is what the spikes are against. Because in the regular world most people know they are not supposed to say things like that anymore, but the view still lingers. People thinking their autistic traits (traits which everyone will have if they look for them) equate to autism are (fanfare for the binary thinking:) WRONG!

12.3.7 Is my love like your love?

All my life I have wanted, not to get married, but to be a wife.

For me there is a distinction: it is not about the big day, the white frock, the invites, the guests, the cake and the church.

It is about the *being* of a wife, and about the promise to be that and to continue being that.

I am blessed to have lots of examples around me. My parents met in their youth and have been happily married, genuinely happily (not just enduringly, stoically, married), ever since. My relatives, my friends, abound with examples of happy stable relationships, all steadily totting up the decades.

Recently my partner has pointed out to me what an archaic ambition this is, for a woman to wish to be owned by a man. That marriage stems from gender bias, that my desire to be wed has been conditioned into me, and all sorts of other very reasonable, very true arguments which I do not wish to hear or fully process, because they strip from me something I want. However flawed the basis of that wanting is. I am not ready to give up on wanting to be a wife.

My diagnosis of autism has been like being handed a magnifying glass with which to reinspect life. Today another layer was peeled back and I am writing as I begin to look at what is presenting at this level of magnification.

As well as being biased by gender, am I being biased by a neurotypical model of love?

You see, I was married, to a lovely man, who remains a lovely man, but who after a few years pointed out to me that being married to him seemed to take something away from me, seemed to make me sad. And being a lovely man, he did not want that so he set me free. I did not want setting free, I wanted to be a wife, but it is like being a bird in a loving hand: you might want to stay but your nature is to fly and I flew.

So those models of marriage around me, that I so cherish and hold up on high. Are they actually something that matches with me?

One couple I know fall asleep in each other's arms every night. Another [couple] choose, on a three-seater sofa, to always sit with one of them on the centre seat. It is this nearness I see and aspire to.

I enjoy physical affection, but I wonder if it is the continuity [that] I find difficult. Like ... right now I would love a hug, but would I want one every day? I do not honestly know. I think so ... maybe that is not it ...

As is becoming my habit: I am writing without answers, looking to see what I'll discover as my fingers trace the keys. So here is another thing, one I will pitch towards the community to see if you can make sense of it:

I can do relationships when they are not in my life, but as soon as they become a joint life they begin to sour.

For example, in my relationship before this one: when we met, I was going through the process of moving house and had nowhere to call home. He lived in a small one-room apartment. I moved in, with just a few things. He cleared a drawer for my clothes, I put a toothbrush in the bathroom and a small toiletries bag on the windowsill. Everything about the way our lives ran was down to his pre-existing life. I just moved in and went with it. I lived by his rules.

We lived happily in that room for over a year, then we tried to live together in my new house and suddenly he was wrong for me.

129

When I met my current partner, we lived hundreds of miles apart. So I travelled up and lived in his house, this time living out of a suitcase, and it worked. But now, living together, I feel too seen to do anything, even though he would mostly approve of the things I naturally do, I am paralysed and do nothing.

If being autistic does not match with ordinary notions of romantic love and long-lasting partnerships what is our ideal to aspire to?

12.3.8 Friend or symptom?

Today I watched a video online in which world-renowned Asperger's expert Tony Attwood[162] described more of my childhood than I feel comfortable admitting.

I cannot say it made me realise, as I have probably known since my diagnosis, but it tipped a balance in my head, pulled a curtain aside, so that I finally admitted to myself that the most significant friendship of my life, one spanning 30 years, is a result of an autistic obsession.

Age seven, I knew I was not doing the social thing correctly. For a year I drew a diary. Each night drawing a picture of what it might be like to have a friend, and annotating it with things we might do together.

I never aimed to be popular, I did not draw huge crowds of friends. Just one. One trusted other in a confusing frightening social world.

By eight I had found her. She is extraordinary. Clever. Beautiful. Willing to brave anything, try anything, with all the guts I lack. We beat each other in maths, always ahead of everyone else in class. She beat me in sports. I beat her in art. I learned everything about her. I obsessed. I fought to have her as my best friend, the highest of accolades for young girls. And eventually I won.

I won through reason. Explaining to her why being my friend was what she should do. Explaining it in an indisputable way so that she conceded.

My family resented the lengths that I went to in order to worship her. They were wrong. They did not understand how incredible she was.

We have remained best friends for over 30 years. In all this time she has stayed as radiant in my mind as when I first spotted her. (And I have secretly cherished that title of 'best friend' as proudly as any seven-year-old, dropping it casually into conversations whenever I can: "oh yes, we are best friends".)

And then I got diagnosed.

And I heard Tony Attwood explain how autistic girls will play with dolls to map out social situations. I did not do that. I planned my friendship on paper, literally drawing diagrams and then I acted it out.

I demanded it of her.

The friendship is real, we have been loyal (a trait I insisted on with some venom and much judgement during our teens). Through the decades, through drug abuse, divorce, ill-advised tattoos, religious extremism, children, parties, eating disorders, self-harm, and even DIY, we have remained friends.

But the foundations of our friendship have been removed. I thought we were friends because she was so extraordinary, but we are friends because I am autistic.

She is ordinary. I look at her now and she is ordinary. She holds a few political views I find difficult. She has been happily married for years, her husband is her best friend. I am a polite admission.

How much of me through the years has been a performance of reality? How many more things can I demand she understand? I have controlled the relationship so far, what if I let go, what would be real?

I believe what will happen is [that] work will move me to a new town in the new year, far enough away that I may visit her a couple of times a year. She will not visit me. Not because she does not like me, but because if I am visiting there will be no need. That is it, that is all there will be.

... Ah, but it is not all so.

Even through the haze of this reality check she still twinkles.

She *is* extraordinary.

Incidentally, Attwood is not the only researcher to have looked into the ways in which autistic girls form relationships; Sedgewick et al.[86] report that autistic girls may become fixated on one person in particular, and focus on making that person their best, and only, friend. The Yellow Ladybugs Project[163] in Australia, which focuses on autistic girls, notes an over-reliance on one friend and problems coping without them as one of their nine descriptors of autism in girls. Sedgewick et al.[86] comment that relationships formed in this manner can be very intense for both parties and can lead to a breakdown of the relationship. Looking back now, I think this stands as a testimony to the brilliance and strength of my best friend: she has withstood my intensity beautifully through three decades and counting worth of friendship.

13   Reflection

This chapter marks a turning point in writing the book. As you can tell at the start, I set out to neatly document a journey from awareness of difference to autistic identity, taking in the landmarks of the post autism diagnosis landscape along the way. But as I wrote this chapter, I realised that the journey was not going as smoothly as I had anticipated: I had stalled.

As I looked back at what my life was like when I wrote part two of the blog, I expected it to stand in stark comparison with my current life. I expected to see myself now embracing and accepting my autistic identity, but I did not. I expected to have more of an understanding of autism and myself than I did at the point of diagnosis, but whether I did or not, and whether some things remained hidden from me – by myself (like Zaphod in section 10.7) or not, remained in question.

Ultimately my sister interceded, forcing my hand to write even more honestly and openly than before.

13.1 Looking back

Re-reading my old blog posts is a painful process. I remember how split my home and work life were back then.

Professionally I was thriving: I was a keynote speaker at big education conferences, I did my first international event for a setting in Australia. I was actively involved in the research community. Flo Longhorn, a hero of mine, invited me to tour alongside her and I began to set up and run my own events.

It was during this time that I first identified myself as autistic in my professional life. I did so in response to being invited to be an ambassador for the super-inclusive sporting event Parallel London (now Parallel Lifestyle www.parallellifestyle.com). To have hidden being autistic at an event that so excels at embracing everyone would have felt hypocritical. In photos of me from the event I can see a nervousness in my eyes and a tension in my fingers that speaks of how hyper aware I was that people might know.

Work was going better than I had ever imagined it could and I was thrilled with it all. Having relied solely on two smart dresses for presenting in up until this point, I began buying frocks. I was so delighted with each opportunity that came my way that I felt like I sparkled. I was connecting with people and actively helping people. My social media networks grew and populated themselves with people pushing for a more inclusive and understanding society.

The people I met online and in life showed me exceptional kindness and support. They continue to do so. I was never nervous about speaking in public, what I said seemed to resonate with people; they liked my words. My overwhelming feeling was always one of gratitude, for being understood and for having the opportunities that came my way. I was working on what would become my second book, and my words were further published in a great many articles in print and online media.

At home, things were very different. The anonymous blog posts were written in ragged bits of frayed time. The tension between my partner and myself resonated through the house like a high-pitched wail about to shatter glass. He was, and is, a remarkable and brilliant man. He, like me, gave his all to making our relationship work. The blog recalls fractious moments, but we were of course fighting for something worth fighting for, and there were other moments of great effort, tenderness and even laughter which did not get recorded.

I remember our shared desperation as we tried over and over to stop our ship from sinking, but there were too many holes in the hull that we could not see, and we argued over how to plug the visible ones. In the end we were both too exhausted to continue.

The sinking of that ship meant that a one-and-a-half-year-old little boy with big bright clear eyes ceased to live in a house with a

Mummy *and* a Daddy and began a life where he lives with Mummy *or* Daddy.

My life changed from one where I got to kiss my son goodnight every night as he went to bed, and kiss him again as he slept on my own way to bed, to one where for half the nights in a week I look in on an empty bedroom. I adjust cuddly toys on an unslept-in bed. I feel as though I have lost half of my child.

Ask either of us and we will cite an irreparable breakdown of communication as the cause of the ending of a love affair that lasted for six years. That assessment is accurate, but I do wonder how we would have fared if we had both had a better understanding of autism.

Not every problem was communication, but had we had the ability to communicate about our problems we would have stood a better chance at fixing them. Communication was the glue we did not have.

Jeremey describes similar difficulties in his relationship in pop out box 22, whilst other people manage to navigate the neurodivergent divide happily; see pop out boxes: 38–42.

22

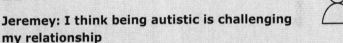

Jeremey: I think being autistic is challenging my relationship

My current relationship has had challenges due to what I think is me being autistic. I have appealed for understanding, tried to describe my difficulties but my partner continues to react to me as he would to anyone else.

Too many inputs

As I've described, social interaction takes brain work. I imagine it's not something that comes that hard to other people; if it did, they wouldn't enjoy gathering in

big social groups. If I am doing one or more things – for example, cooking dinner, or listening to music – then my mind is occupied with working on these. In these situations, if I get asked a question, I tend to answer "like a robot" as I have been told. I lose the relaxed speed of speech, the normal musicality of speech that people have and I just answer correctly, accurately, minimally and quickly. My partner doesn't like it and will say, "Oh, too many inputs?" almost mockingly.

Answering first

I answer my partner's questions before he has finished asking them, which he finds infuriating. In a normal situation he would start talking and I would switch attention to listening. In doing this I will leave a normal conversational pause and then answer. If I have other inputs that I can't stop (in the middle of working something out, concentrating on reading something, etc.), I often answer before he has finished his thought and that is something that people do not like. They like to be heard, they like for people to consider answers.

I do not mean to be dismissive of him when I answer a question he is still in the process of asking. It is just how I am when I do not filter myself using the rules of conversation. I understand the need for those rules, I just do not have the brain space to use them at the same time as concentrating on something else. I understand his frustration because I hate being talked over.

Being talked over

If I'm explaining something, or expressing myself and I am talked over, I just stop … I can't continue talking as I have to listen. This means that meetings are very difficult for me as I have to wait for a silent gap in order to speak. In a meeting with lots of active discussion it is almost impossible for me to speak. There can be three conversations going on simultaneously, but everyone knows what's going on and there are zero gaps of silence. I am impressed by their skill, but I may as well not be in the room.

Being talked over for me means that the person doesn't value me as a person, but if you answer my question before I finish – then thank you! You have saved me the time and I have my answer sooner than expected.

If you talk over me when I am trying to express myself, then I understand that to mean that you don't care what I have to say. Your interruption also presents another problem to me: I have worked out this sentence and I want to deliver it, if I get cut off, I will start again, cut me off again and I will start again. I need to get to the end. It was important enough for me to start so I have to finish it.

I have to finish my sentence

One incident happened during the February half-term this year. I had come upstairs just to ask my partner if they could do something (I can't even remember what it was). The sentence must have been about six words long, he cut me off halfway to dismiss it. I started again. He cut me off again. This repeated a few more times, each time I stepped up a level. From a very calm, happy half-term holiday morning person, until I reached a point where I had completely lost it.

I feel the need to say that I am generally a really happy, easygoing, decent person ... but when I say I lost it, I mean 100%. I am embarrassed by it. I lost control. My conscious self was just watching what was happening as a non-involved observer.

I couldn't speak. I came downstairs and smashed the remote control. I went into the kitchen and pressed myself against the wall. I clutched my head which vibrated like it had electricity surging through it. It took a while before I could walk. I made it to the sofa (still holding my head). I sat down to try to calm myself. It was the worst I think I have ever been. I left the house and came back three days later.

23

Risk of abuse within relationships, based on the work of Chapman[164]

TW

In 2017, neurodiversity advocate, researcher and lecturer Robert Chapman, whose work focuses on the implications of the concept of neurodiversity for understanding health and wellbeing, identified autistic adults as more likely to be at increased risk of domestic abuse than neurotypical adults.

Chapman (para. 21) reports leading autism researcher Tony Attwood stating that "people with autism are susceptible and vulnerable to domestic abuse in relationships" and commenting that researchers have yet to establish why "those with autism seem to be a magnet which attracts predators, not only from bullying and teasing at school, but also relationship predators". Chapman cites a plethora of research that indicates strikingly high rates of mis-treatment of autistics by trusted others; for example, friends, peers and colleagues (see pop out boxes 21: 'Bullying'; and 25: 'Autistic people are at increased risk of sexual abuse' for examples here). He reasons that against such a backdrop it is unsurprising that trusted partners could also pose a risk.

In his article 'We Need to Talk about the Domestic Abuse of Autistic Adults',[164] Chapman remarks on how research has failed to tackle this paradigm and speculates that perhaps academics whose views are founded in historic characterisations of autistics as unfeeling are not expecting autistic people to enter into relationships. He recounts how he used online autistic forums to tentatively explore the topic and was inundated with messages from autistic people reporting domestic abuse.

Chapman observes three common themes to the accounts of abuse presented to him:

1. The trusting nature of autistics was used to gain control over them.
2. 'Gaslighting', a subtle yet pervasive form of psychological manipulation was used to make the victim doubt their own lived reality, often including doubting the validity of their own feelings.
3. Abusive partners often convinced family and friends that the autistic partner was the controlling one, sometimes by playing on misleading stereotypes regarding autism.

Autistics who had experienced abuse within relationships reported to Chapman "the relevance of factors they took to be characteristic of being autistic" (para. 24):

- "We want to see the best in everyone, especially those we care about." (para. 24)
- "We might be more easily gaslighted, because some of us can be very emotionally sensitive, so it can lead us to wonder if we're overreacting." (para. 25)
- "Due to years of conditioning I automatically think a problem is my fault and try to fix it." (para. 26)

Chapman (para. 26) concludes: "Society already systematically gaslights autistic people, and so we can internalize this oppression and thus become more susceptible to the same tactic from manipulative individuals."

Chapman's observations tie in with the vulnerabilities highlighted by Milton's[62] double empathy work (discussed here in pop out box 19) and are reflected by other commentators who cite autistic people as being particularly susceptible to gaslighting (see pop out box 14: 'Gaslighting').

Jeremey's account of his experience of meltdown (see pop out box 22: 'Jeremey: I think being autistic is challenging my relationship') echoes issues raised by Chapman's work.

13.2 Looking forward – acceptance

As I write today, I am heavily pregnant and I am married to a man I love a great deal. Life is very different now to how it was when I was writing my blog. The prospect of history repeating itself is terrifying.

The patterns laid out in my diagnosis document are clear: my capabilities and my limits. I still fail the Sally Anne Test regularly. I still feel suffocated by little things being out of place in the house. How can I be sure things really are so different?

Every time I have embarked on a new relationship, I have imagined that it would be different. That this time, *this time*, I will be able through a sheer act of will to not be autistic. Not to misunderstand. Not to mind. I am yet to accept autistic as my state of being, and so I am condemned to wasting energy trying to change it.

Whether autism is a difference or disability has become the crux of my willingness to accept it as a part of myself (I sound like my father – see pop out box 4: 'My father: I am not autistic'). But quite clearly it should be accepted either way: I should simply recognise that it *is*.

Difference = good, disability = bad, is yet another example of my binary thinking at play. Recognising autism as an *is* would be far easier if there was also a societal understanding of what it is (something Noleta comments on the lack of in pop out box 1: 'Noleta, 15 years old: my diagnosis is my dark secret'). With acceptance, I could try to navigate life as I am, rather than frittering energy away on trying to be otherwise.

Would acceptance, from myself more so than from others, see me stop viewing my mind which (in the words of the diagnosis report) has "an unusually strong drive and ability to systemise" as petty? Would I then invest energy in the skill sets I have, rather than draining it in trying to acquire the ones I lack?

Another aspect crucial to my being willing to accept being autistic is admitting to difficulties. To be very clear and avoid misunderstandings, I do not in any way think that being disabled is bad. The "disability = bad" (above) is not a value judgement on disability, it is a reflection of the binary options for thought in my head. As I said in section 2.7: being autistic clearly is a disability to some and an ability to others: it is a spectrum (something rather ironically my black and white mind fails to grasp).

In my mind, something has to be good and something has to be bad. If I could settle myself to autism being a simple difference, then it wins the good slot and I would accept and defend it. If I find that autism is a deficit, then it is a disability and wins the bad slot and I will not accept it, not because to be disabled is bad but because I personally am unwilling to admit to facing any difficulties.

I am very aware of how privileged and comfortable my life is; to admit to struggling feels like spitting in the face of those with real difficulties. Other people lead far more challenged lives. Those people are not remote to me, they are a part of my thinking every day. As a student I took part in short-term aid work projects in developing countries. I know how lucky (and it is lucky because I did not do anything to gain this privilege) I am to have clean water every day. I have not left a tap running since I met those people: they would never waste a drop of such a precious resource.

My work brings me into contact with a great many life-limited children and their families, and they teach me time and time

141

again how precious this moment now is. I have been to too many children's funerals. I have seen incredibly strong people wring every ounce of life out of the time they got to spend with their loved ones. It is offensive by comparison to struggle to spend time with those I love. Again, admitting to such a luxury of a problem feels like insulting those with real problems.

The self-pity I feel as I look in on my little boy's empty bedroom is disgusting, not only in comparison to those families whose children will never sleep in their beds again, but in comparison to close friends who have battled through IVF treatment until they could go no further, friends whose sexuality makes the prospect of having a child so much more complicated, and friends whose children died before birth, one of whom should have been two days older than my son, but died two days before her birthday. My son sleeps in his bed and I should be nothing but grateful.

My life is very much a privileged one, full of love, supportive parents and good friends. I have never wanted for money or food. It is very much an easy ride. It is not a life that warrants *any* claim of difficulty. Why should I be tired? What is there to find a struggle? I have no right to those emotions. (There are those "rigid rules around emotions" that the psychologist wrote about in my diagnosis report – section 9.2 – I have good reason for them!)

13.3 Everyone

TW

"But you have to point out how hard that makes things for you, in order to explain that aspect of autism."

My sister has called me on Skype to find out how writing this book is going and I have complained that I do not want it to read as navel gazing. I want to use my experience as an example, but not have things be about me.

For my sister to say something so direct is rare. She is a Quaker: she listens rather than speaks (quite the contrast to me) and spends her free time reading hulking great books on complicated subjects that I could never fathom, nor have the patience to even attempt to tackle. Consequently, she is far wiser than I am and far less likely to tell a person what they should do. Her respect for people and her belief in the inherent value of life are clear in all her actions.

I gave all the reasons in 13.2 for why I have no claim to life being hard. My sister is infuriating to argue with. She does not speak back, she just lets your words hang in the air until you realise how foolish you sound. All my nice neat pre-crafted responses did nothing to shift her calm steady gaze.

Finally, in petulant tones I spat out the real answer: "I don't want to admit I struggle because it is true."

(Perhaps this is a primitive survival instinct in me: admit a weakness and the herd might leave you behind to be eaten by predators).

Though not well crafted, and not justifiable, that statement is true on many levels. It is not about measuring the hardships I have faced against anyone else's. It is about my unwillingness to admit need of any kind.

I have to be in control. To admit a need or a weakness, however small, even just to say something like, "I have an itch on my shoulder blade", is an absolute no for me. In my binary mind, admissions of vulnerability are off the cards. Admitting weakness offers power to someone else. Even to say I have an itch or need a wee rescinds control in some small way from me to whomever I say it to.

Through childhood and adolescence and near faultlessly to the present day, I have only admitted to difficulties after I have dealt with them. I tended to my own cuts and grazes. I refused to be taken to the member of staff on playground duty for a plaster. When I got my first period, I dealt with it myself without telling my mother or turning to friends for guidance. When I have been admitted to hospital with scary infections, I have only told family and friends about the experience after I have been discharged, and then only once I was fully well.

My lived life is an open book.

The life I am living now only I know about.

The anthem of my toddler years, often quoted to me by people who knew me then – "I'll do it myself!" – has resonated throughout my whole life. I am loath to admit to difficulties that stand to be ongoing, that could indicate that I cannot do it all myself. Incidentally, this is a trait I share in common with other autistic girls; Sarah Wild Head of Limspfield Grange, a school for autistic girls, cites not asking for help and masking their difficulties as being characteristic of the girls in attendance at her school.[71]

Every life is a struggle. The things I find difficult do not warrant special attention, they just happen to be mine. If I wrote about them, it would feel like I was claiming a particular need when I do not in any way see my own need to be greater than anyone else's. Very much the opposite in fact. The needs I see around me are far greater than my own and that's where our attention and energy should lie. Stating a difficulty feels like asking for help and I do not want any help: I'll do it myself!

If I say being autistic causes me to struggle, that is an insult to autism is it not?

I do not want to risk sounding like the keyboard warriors hammering out tweets in caps lock slating the neurotypical community for their lack of awareness of autism and demanding change. If being neurotypical was a diagnosis too, I am sure there would be a related pattern of struggles and a great many "severely neurotypical" people whose lives were far harder than my own.

Incidentally, I think the idea of a neurotypical diagnosis has legs. There are neurotypical people whose exceptional social skills enable them to get on in life where others would fail. There are neurotypical people whose reliance on others for their own emotional stability is at times debilitating. The pathologising of autism feeds into prejudiced views of it as something that is undesirable.

I want to defend the community. If I am to claim identity, I want to claim it in the positive, not claim it through displaying weakness. I am not going to play into the hands of people who offer 'cures'. With everything so ill-defined, so misunderstood, I feel defensive and protective over the notion of neurodivergence. And I feel this all the more on behalf of those living more challenged lives than myself.

My sister laughed at me, recognising my unchanging nature. If you know me online, you will probably recognise it too. There is a relentlessly positive spin to the posts I write. I was once told by a digital strategist, who was presenting after me at a librarian's conference, that online you have only two choices: you can be a cheerleader or you can be a troll. I am very much the cheerleader. Not solely because you would have to torture me before I admitted to struggling, but because I feel very defensive of humanity in general.

I imagine everyone to be vulnerable and trying their best. I want to recognise their efforts and cheer them on, not goad them when they slip up. In doing that perhaps I give the game away. The diagnosis says I am prone to believing that everyone thinks as I do. In failing the Sally Anne Test, I show my belief that people know and think what I know and think.

The truth is that I am a vulnerable person who is doing their best, and I have no idea who anyone else is.

"You are an interesting test subject," I said to my sister.

"Because of the controlled variables?" she smiled.

"Yes! You're socially awkward" (she is a senior research librarian and all your preconceptions about what a person in that role might be like are probably accurate when it comes to my sister). "You were brought up in the same way as me, by the same people as me. That's nurture accounted for. And you're not autistic."

"No," she agreed.

I pondered for a moment on how we might do a comparative measure of how much we had each struggled with life. Then I hit upon what felt at the time like an easy option:

"How many times in your life would you say you've been suicidal?" I asked, fishing around for a rough estimate on her part.

She laughed again, this time shocked more than tickled. "Never."

It was my turn to be shocked. "What? Never? … Really? Not ever?"

"No," she reiterated, a little more slowly, leaving me time for what she was saying to sink in. "Not ever."

"Oh." I was too stunned to find more words than that.
After a while she ventured: "Should I ask the same of you?"

"Loads of times," I said, in the same tone I would have used if she had asked me how many times I had drunk a cup of tea. "I always find life a bit of a struggle. Everyone does."

My "Everyone does" tailed off, sounding weak after her so certain "Never".

Realising that people do not feel like me, do not think like me, has become a familiar feeling, but it is no less isolating, no less desolate for being so.

We are sisters. Surely we are alike?

She looked at me and waited, as I realised once again that I am different. Not in a big or dramatic way. Just that my version of life might not be the 'everyone' experience I like to think it is.

24

Health inequalities and more

TW

Autistic people face barriers to health care access that are not faced by neurotypical people.[57,104,132,165] General practitioners report finding it harder to treat autistic patients.[166] Non-neuro-normative expression of emotion, pain and other symptoms can lead to mis-diagnosis or lack of treatment.[167-170] A study conducted in Scotland[171] found autistic adults five times more likely than the general population to be in poor health. Intersectionality of autism with age and gender is also noted as the study observes older people and female autistics to be more likely to experience poor health. The study draws the shocking conclusion that autism has a greater influence on poor health than ageing.

Health inequalities are just one example of the many life inequalities faced by autistic people. In pop out boxes 7, 11, 23, 17, 21, 25, and you can read about inequalities relating to mental health, life expectancy, bullying, abuse, suicide and employment.

Researchers exploring inequalities experienced by autistic people report findings across a wide range of areas: Autistic people are more likely to have been bullied or to have had adverse life experiences than neurotypical people.[172-173] They are at increased risk of abuse, neglect and loneliness[174] and are likely to experience a lower quality of life than their peers.[175]

Taken individually, each finding of inequality can seem shocking, but viewed as a whole, with an understanding that to be autistic puts you in a minority group within a society set up for a majority group, they are less so. The neurotypical majority think, sense and express themselves differently. We all understand that to be in a misunderstood minority puts you at an automatic disadvantage in life. With this understanding in place, you are less surprised when confronted with extraordinary demonstrations of society's lack of understanding; for example, when (for a brief period) the DVLA[176] drew the attention of the Equality and Human Rights Commission after it decided that autistic people should have to declare their autism on their driver's licence, informing them that failure to do so could result in fines of up to £1000 and invalidation of their car insurance despite autism having absolutely no bearing on one's ability to drive.

25

Autistic people are at increased risk of sexual abuse

TW

Research has consistently found autistic people to be more at risk of sexual abuse than their neurotypical peers.[172,177–178] Studies have shown autistic children to be at increased risk of sexual abuse with findings indicating that they are two or three times more likely than peers to be victims of abuse.[179–181] Edelson[182] highlights that autistic children may be at further risk due to 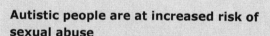barriers to their being able to report abuse brought about by communication differences.

Autistic women have been found to be more at risk of sexual abuse than autistic men[183] which is not surprising when considered against the heightened vulnerability of women in general to becoming victims of sexual assault (a survey conducted by the UK Ministry of Justice, the Home Office and the Office for National Statistics found that 20% of women had experienced some form of sexual abuse compared to 4% of men[184]). However, further studies have shown autistic women to be at increased risk of sexual abuse when compared to women who are not autistic.[173,185-186]

Personally, I have been assaulted more than half a dozen times, none of them are incidents I care to reflect on in any great detail, but of them all there is only one where I could say that being autistic did not play a role. My misunderstanding of signals and my atypical responses to situations have contributed to how at risk I have been. My functional understanding of the rules of communication have drawn me into interactions that others would have avoided: when my assailant instigated conversation that appeared to conform to expected norms, I felt obliged to provide the expected response. In this situation, my decision to stay and talk, when inside I wanted to run, gave them the chance to get a secure hold of my hair, one they did not give up for a further terrifying 45 minutes.

Choices I have made, and continue to make, to accommodate my autism put me at risk; for example, I will always walk across an unfamiliar town rather than catch a taxi as I am daunted by the prospect of an unplanned conversation with a taxi driver. Within relationships, my inability at times to express emotion, and the challenges I face finding words for feelings, have meant that there have been times when intimate moments have been shared in a non-consensual fashion. I do not count these moments as abusive as

> there was no intent to abuse from my partners and every one of them would have stopped if I had said, "stop". But the memory of those moments feels like mould in my heart and has had its impact in other places in my life; for example, breastfeeding my son in the small hours of the night. Being woken up, wishing you were still asleep and having to give your nipple over to someone is a situation in which it is easy for memories to get muddled. I got through it by focusing on podcasts and social media, but had I been able to articulate my emotions in my relationships, or had partners known I was autistic and looked for my atypical communication, perhaps those could have been intimate happy moments shared between my child and me.

13.4 Life

TW

Life is beautiful.

I am constantly dazzled by life, especially by the people living it.

In Chris Packham's 2017 documentary *Asperger's and Me*,[187] he is filmed standing outside amidst the nature that he loves. He describes how it feels to him as if the world is in high definition, a hyper reality: too loud, too bright, too overwhelming. He does not hate nature in any way. He loves it. But in some ways, it is too much for him. This is how I feel about people: their humanity, their brilliance, their frailty, their beauty and their kindness are often too much for me. I do not dislike life in any way. Life and those living it are staggeringly beautiful in my eyes.

There was a cheesy pop song released around the time I was training to be a teacher called 'Just a ride' by Jem.[95] The analogy in the song, of life as a journey with a beginning and end along a rollercoaster of emotional ups and downs, is an old one.

It is unusual that I notice a song. I stopped listening to music in my early twenties. No longer able to take the emotional punch it can land and more aware of a need to be responsible for my mental health than I had been before. I do not keep any music in my house. I do not have digital music files on my devices. My radio is tuned to BBC Radio 4, so I only hear songs if they are featured on *Desert Island Discs* or play in stores when I am shopping.

If a song lodges in my mind, there is usually a reason for it (as I explained in 11.2.1). For this song, the reason for it registering was simple: it encapsulated how I think about life.

Life is *just* a ride. It is not a terrible horrific unbearable ride. It is *just* a ride. It is not, to me, sacred or particularly precious. It is *just* a ride. I find it dazzling and beautiful at times, and hard at other times. But it remains *just* a ride. And … if it were all the same to everyone else: I would like to get off now please.

I have felt that way about life for around 30 years. It is a feeling now complicated by having children. I have lifted people onto this ride with me, and although my preference is still to disembark, I recognise that it is my responsibility to supervise their ride. I am writing this, so it is clear I did not get off the ride. But there have been times when that indifference between being and not being has been skewed by circumstances and I have considered what it would take to disembark early.

Self-harm was never an attempt to get off the ride. It was done to stay on board. Although a light cut across a wrist once could classify as exploring options.

At times I have gathered equipment and driven to remote locations. I have written carefully worded goodbye letters.

I know that getting off the ride is not allowed. In many ways it is my autistic brain that keeps me safe. Its dogged adherence to rule keeping, the binary thinking, makes it very clear: suicide is wrong.

Is this undercurrent of effort and exhaustion present in every life?

I believe it is.

But I am an unreliable narrator.

Looking in from the outside, can you imagine a life where an acceptance of being autistic, and having an understanding of what that meant, created periods of rest?

26

Life expectancy

TW

Hirvikoski et al.[125] matched 27,122 autistic people with neurotypical peers over a 12-year period. They found the autistic people to be two and a half times more likely to die than their counterparts during the period of the study. The rates for autistic women were even higher (for women with high support needs, the rates were nine times those of their neurotypical peers). The study reported an average age of death for autistic people to be 53 years compared to 70 years for the general population.

The study noted epilepsy (which is more common in autistic people than in neurotypical people) and suicide (reported to be seven and a half times more likely in autistic people than in neurotypical people) to be standout causes of death. Other studies[188-189] have also cited heart problems as a leading cause of death and speculated as to whether this could be due to the increased stress levels that come from being autistic in a non-autistic world. The researchers indicate health inequalities as a likely contributing factor in the relatively high suicide rates of autistic people and in their increased risk of dying from illnesses such as cancer or serious infections where issues, for example, in communicating symptoms could result in poorer outcomes.

A comparable study[190] that matched autistic people to neurotypical people over a 33-year period found similar results; reporting autistic people to be nearly twice as likely to die as neurotypical people, and noting autistic women to be at particularly high risk; and commenting on the complex relationship between autism and health inequalities. Further studies[189,191-194] report similar patterns: autistic people are more likely to die ahead of their neurotypical peers, with autistic women being particularly at risk.

Often the sample groups used for these studies are autistic people with higher support needs, meaning that their findings are not necessarily reflective of the autistic population as a whole. However, studies that focus on autistics with low support needs – for example, those diagnosed in adulthood[195] or women with autistic traits[196] – have also found significantly increased vulnerabilities. Regardless of high or low support needs, autistic people experience mortality rates in excess of their neurotypical peers.

To be clear: studies do not suggest that people die from being autistic. Autistic people die of epilepsy, suicide, cancer, infections and so on. Their risks of dying from these conditions is heightened by factors including the inequalities they experience due to a lack of understanding of autism.

27

Suicide risk factors

TW

Research finds autistic people to be significantly more likely to die from, or attempt, suicide than neurotypical people.[112,118–119,121–130,197–199] Those considered to have lower support needs (sometimes referred to as 'high functioning' – a term rejected by the autistic community; or 'Asperger's' – a diagnostic category that is being retired) are at greater risk of dying by or attempting suicide than those viewed as having high support needs.[195,201-202] Additionally, some studies have noted autistic women to be at particular risk of suicide when compared to neurotypical women, or to autistic men[195–197]).

Commentators have sought to account for the relatively high suicide risk rates amongst autistics with low support needs and autistic women by linking their risks to their increased awareness of their position in society. The logic being that this increased awareness motivates masking and causes the low self-esteem and feelings of lack of belonging that are all known risk factors for suicide. This may well be true, but it is also worth considering that those with high support needs are more likely to live supervised lives and therefore have less opportunity to act on any suicidal thoughts. Furthermore, the methods used by studies reporting these findings are inaccessible for people with high support needs, meaning that they do not take part or someone else answers for them. Horowitz et al.[203] draw attention to the need for developmentally appropriate screening tools for non-verbal autistics in relation to suicidal thoughts. Researchers[112] note that autistic people have often been purposefully excluded from research into mental health, this exclusion from research is a risk factor in itself and could well be one that is especially pertinent to non-verbal autistics.

Sadly, some studies, carefully not referenced here, still seek to identify flaws in the autistic person that need correcting in order to remediate their suicide risk. These studies ignore the 'if it walks like a duck and quacks like a duck' logic that could easily be deployed to account for the vulnerability of autistics to suicide. It is already well-established that having good self-esteem, feeling like you belong and can be yourself, and being able to reach out to a trusted someone for help are all protective factors against suicide.

Researchers have[204-205] demonstrated masking to be associated with increased suicide risk in autistics. The significance of self-esteem in relation to suicide ideation in general and specifically with regard to adult autistics has been highlighted.[206] Researchers[120] demonstrated that not feeling as though they belonged in society put autistic people at increased risk of suicide. Various researchers[207-209] point to differences in the capabilities of professionals in meeting the needs of neurotypicals compared to autistics: they lack tools for identifying suicide risks in autistics and they lack a clear understanding of autism in relation to mental health, particularly with regard to differences in presentation and communication of mental health issues between autistics and neurotypicals. These findings all indicate societal differences which mean that autistic people are less likely to have someone to reach out to, less likely to be spotted as being in need, less likely to feel like they belong and less likely to have good self-esteem. If it walks like a duck and it quacks like a duck, then maybe the problem is not in the autistics themselves but in the society in which they are trying to survive.

13.5 Suicide

TW

In the previous section (13.4), I mentioned self-harm as being preferable to the alternative. I was of course referring to suicide. Statistics tell us suicide is more common amongst autistics than neurotypicals, but they do not tell us why.

Is it that autistic minds are more easily broken?

Is it that we are less suited to life?

Is it the pressure to conform?

Is it a glitch in our thinking?

The knowledge that it is more common for autistics to kill themselves than it is for those who are not autistic to do so alerts us to a problem, but does not tell us how to solve that problem. To solve the problem, we would need to know why this disparity exists.

I can only speak for myself. For myself, I view any moment in time as a choice. I might wake at the start of a day and consider my options for that day: what could I do? Well, I could go to the shops, I could do some work, I could go for a walk, or I could kill myself. It is always on my list because it is always, from a factual point of view, a possibility.

In mental health terms, thinking of suicide, without any intent to die by suicide, is in itself a diagnosable feature of mental illness. By this reckoning I am mentally ill, and have been mentally ill since I first understood what suicide was aged eight. But I think the reckoning is based on a neurotypical model of mental health, based on brains that respect taboo topics and do not go near them. Brains in which the possibility of a self-inflicted death would never cross one's mind.

I think of suicide every day, not in a morbid way, just in a very perfunctory factual way. Thinking of suicide is not a sign that I am upset or stressed. Even on the happiest of days it is an option. What a lovely day to die!

I wonder, though, whether having the card already on the table puts me a step or two closer to acting on that possibility than someone who would never ordinarily think of it, and for whom that thought would only be prompted by the most extreme of life's circumstances.

I am also aware of my mind's capacity to fix on a topic and explore it to the nth degree. Were it to ever fix on that particular topic, that could be a very dangerous train of thought to be on. The case of Callie Lewis[210] stands as an illustration of suicide ideation happening to an autistic woman, and researchers[211] have also looked at the same thing happening to autistic men.

As alluded to in section 13.4: 'Life', there have been times in my life when I have been suicidal. Including more than one occasion when I have taken actions with the intention of getting off the ride. Those times are almost more alarming for how clear they are in my mind, how calmly they were decided upon. Research[195] indicates that 35% of autistics have planned or attempted suicide.

I did not approach suicide with a chaotic desperate mind, I looked at the options, thought about them clearly and rationally. I chose to sweep aside the churning mass of 'supposed tos' and social pressures and just consider myself. I asked myself what I would choose if I were choosing for myself alone and concluded that I would like to go.

Here is life, and here is not life. I recognise that life has many adventures to be had and I enjoy many aspects of it, I have nothing against life. But if I could choose, then I would get off the ride. Thank you, that is plenty for me, I have had a lovely time, let someone else have a turn. It is a thought born out of honesty. Not misery or desperation or even insanity, unless you are prepared to believe that certain thoughts are inherently insane. I am well acquainted with the noisy landscape of my mind, I know what it is like when it tends towards madness and I know how it sounds when it is sane, and it is the calm sane mind that says: "enough".

In my twenties, I got angry with the people around me who cared about me. It is often said that suicide is a selfish act, and I know that for me it would be. I doubt that it is true for everyone. When I think of the people I have known who have taken their lives, I am pretty sure what each would have wished for was a different life, not the end of life.

On the occasions that I collected equipment and drove to a secluded spot, it was a loyalty to the people around me that stopped me from acting on my own will. I did not act, but I was furious with them. I looked at what each got from my being alive: a conversation here, another mouth at the dinner table there. I considered how richly filled the rest of their lives were: they had more than enough people to have conversations with, plenty of bums on seats around the table. I was a tiny fraction of their lives and yet for that tiny fraction they would deny me my right to what I wanted to do with mine.

It reached a head when I wrote my mother a carefully reasoned letter explaining the balance between her gain and what it cost me and asking permission to go. It would be selfish of her to reject the request. And if she could be persuaded to act unselfishly and give me her blessing, then I could go and it would not have been a selfish act on my part. It all felt very clear to me. I read and re-read the letter. The logic was sound, she couldn't argue with it.

Unsurprisingly to those watching from the outside, the clear logic of my letter did not resonate, instead it packed an emotional punch I had not anticipated, causing much upset and worry. I did not get permission. And at that point I figured that if I could not have what I wanted from my life, then I would try and be all they wanted. Some part of me stopped existing then and I have been more useful to other people since. My number one worry if I am tired or worn out is that I have not been useful enough to other people.

14   Blog part three: half a year after diagnosis

Part three of my blog contains posts that stretch over a six-month period. At the start I sound quite resigned and sanguine. A sad inevitability has crept in, I was no longer imagining futures with happily-ever-afters in them. You will spot that I swing between including myself as part of the autistic "tribe" (14.6) and clearly stating I am not like them at all (14.5). Picking up and dropping the identity like a garment I cannot work out how to wear.

Towards the end of the blog, the tension between my partner and me is more apparent and more resolved. I closed the blog as the relationship ended. Without him in the house, the misunderstandings were gone. The tiny details of life – whether the bread bin was left open or closed, and whether specific items were brought to the dinner table – were gone. My pettiness and moral correctness went unchecked.

The first thing I noticed as I began living alone was how much more energy I had, even without having someone to share the gettings up to a small child in the night, or to play with the child whilst dinner was made. I felt superhuman. Without the need to wonder what someone else would think, on top of wondering what I ought to think, I had more capacity for engaging with my son. The world and the people and things in it seemed to leap back into action, as if they had been held on pause or dulled. Everything regained its colour.

I also felt right, and in being so, I felt good. Unchallenged I felt like me again. Retrospectively, I have enormous respect for what my partner tried to do as he reflected my own mind back at me and held up its idiosyncrasies for me to see. As poetic a husband who sets you free sounds, that freedom did not achieve anything. Being challenged was uncomfortable, hurtful, but ultimately fruitful. I am certain there was no malice in his frustrations with me. He wanted me to see myself accurately, so that we could be together as real people, not as performances of people.

14.1 Lacking in the social graces

I am always surprised when I look back of photos of me from my early teens how nice I looked. How much as pretty as the next girl. How unravaged my face.

There was nothing wrong with me, so why did I not fit in?

It is the subtle part of the spectrum. Not out and out failure, just a slight disconnect. Like a train coupling that does not work. The carriages bump together but then one moves and the other is left behind. Other people seemed to meet and then carry on together.

The subtlety of my failing at relationships is as hard to spot as what was going wrong with friendships earlier in life. But today my partner put his finger on it...

One of our first arguments was him saying: "You are not interested in me, you just want a project, someone to fix."

I have projectised many a relationship. They last around two years. It is a good solid amount of time that does not look like failure. I have done the same with friendships.

Tonight he said that since my diagnosis, he has seen aspects of how I relate to him differently. And he gave the projectising as an example: "You studied me, learned everything about me and that felt good at the time, like you were interested in me. But I was a project. I think that is just what you do when you like someone and want to be close to them. You learn everything about them."

Guilty as charged.

But what is it normal people do? Do they not want to learn everything, and understand it? What is missing?

(This pattern of projectising relationships is something Vance[212] writes about in her blog post: 'Why your Asperger's–NT Relationship Is Failing').

14.2 Glass layers

You probably think you know who you are.

Perhaps you know your goals in life.

You know your likes and dislikes.

But study any one of these things in too much detail and it can be unpicked. Why is it you want that thing? Is it because of something that happened to you in life before? If that thing had not happened, had not slightly broken you, you would not need to strive for whatever it is that you want?

Are you really you? Are your likes actually your likes or are they inherited from people you grew up around? Are they because of your cultural climate? Because of your religion?

Is there really any YOU at all?

Look closely? Study it? The harder you look the more transparent things become, and when you understand them in detail you see through them and they vanish. You fall into invisibility.

Autism is another layer of glass for me.

Why am I upset by his remark?

Is it because of me?

Is it because of autism?

How far do you adjust?

I know some people believe the whole world should adapt to them. It is easy to understand the passion behind this belief when you look at lives that have been so thwarted by the neurotypical biases in the world. It is only natural to rail against it. But ultimately, demanding [that] everyone adapt to you is committing the same crime you are upset with other people for committing in the first place.

I could be persuaded that autism, for all its gifts, is some sort of defect, a problem, or illness, and seeing it as such, it would be fair to conclude that all the 'because of autism' choices I make, and feelings I have, should be carefully set aside.

Is it him?

Or is it me?

He says things that hurt me.

Do they hurt me because I am autistic?

If they do, is it fair of me to be hurt?

He is saying things that would not hurt someone else, you can understand why he thinks it unfair that I get cross with him for saying things that are to him – and (nearly) everyone else – perfectly fine.

But he knows me, and I am hurt. He knows that. Is it still fair to say these things? Maybe you are shouting, "No, it is not fair, how mean of him, does [he] not realise that you are AUTISTIC!"

But what if he did change his behaviour, watch his words, walk on eggshells in order to 'mind my autism' as if my autism were broken glass on a floor across which he must walk barefoot?

Then it remains unchallenged. I remain a prisoner to the demands it places on me. He becomes a captive to its whims.

Keep looking, with each swing of the argument, with each additional pane of glass, we feel as if things are getting clearer, they are being understood more,

and more...

and more...

Until they are invisible and we have seen through everything to the nothing beyond.

14.3 All they can be?

"Why don't you just tell them you have Asperger's, and then they would not ask you to do that?" Related to work.

The answer is because I can do it. The questioner is posing the question because they know how much anxiety doing this thing, which they would find so simple as to almost not notice, will cause me.

But I can do it. And if you can, then you should. You should not opt for the easy life. Everyone should strive to be the best that they should be.

Shouldn't they?

"Why don't you tell him that it bothers you?"

This one relates to life at home. The answer is because I know it should not bother me. I know someone else would not be bothered. If I try, I can overcome the being bothered. Being bothered is an unpleasant trait. I do not want to allow myself to have it.

"Gosh, I did not realise. You must be exhausted with trying to appear normal".

Possibly the kindest thing someone has said to me as a result of me revealing my diagnosis.

Does everyone have to be the best they can be?

Ought we to push ourselves to our limits?

Is it especially important that people with disabilities push themselves to be the best that they can be?

Is it ever acceptable to coast?

14.4 Here be dragons

On old maps, in territory yet to be discovered, people wrote "Here be dragons" – as a disclaimer for their ignorance.

As I chart the territory of this part of the autistic spectrum, I look around at some of my fellow Aspie women and fondly wonder if we are the dragons.

Some parts of the spectrum are relatively well mapped. Be clear, this is not a 'woe is me and my uncharted territory' post. Those parts are well mapped because the need was great. My need is subtle.

Clearly there is a landscape, built of the tendencies and the abilities of people with my sort of Autism. I would quite like a name for that, so that I did not feel I was having to

162

define myself against other people on the spectrum. As we move towards numbering, I wonder if we will yet develop the sort of detailed categorisation that the T-athletes in the Paralympics get. Will I be an A32 as opposed to an A2?

I tweet my posts and it is not uncommon for someone to say they have had a similar revelation before and that my journey is the same as theirs in some way. Not that we all walk the same path, lead the same lives, but that the similarity of our internal landscapes means we follow similar routes through life.

I would welcome a map.

When I was diagnosed, I was given a leaflet about Asperger's. A leaflet that was not about me, but was about ... let us be honest, despite its carefully presented gender-neutral position, it was about men on a part of the spectrum that throws up a lot more barriers to inclusion in the neurotypical world. Whereas this part of the spectrum does not exactly stop you from taking part, it just leaves you slightly off kilter when you do.

A leaflet about me would have been gratefully received, some bullet points saying, "Hey, you might feel/do this, this and this, but fear not, you are not actually a dragon."

Actually, that leaflet would really help were I to begin a new relationship. I would like to be able to give someone a handy 'head's up' so that they at least had a sense of what they were getting into.

Of course, I know about some parts of the landscape. The parts of myself that I spotted that took me to the doctors in the first place. But there were other parts of the diagnostic criteria that surprised me. Pre-mapped-out parts that it turned out, unbeknownst to myself, I had. But there are more and working them out alone is tricky.

My life is not particularly challenged. But my challenges are the only ones I can truly do anything about. They might be relatively minor when compared to other people's but they are the obstacles in my path, the ones I have to climb over, and knowing where and what they are would really help as I bimble about the place.

Map suggests a 2D representation of a 3D world.

I think Autism may very well be 4D.

I need a map that charts time too as there are periods of life that hold different challenges to someone who has a condition that is considered a social and communication disorder. And for me it certainly is.

Being a teenager has to be an obvious challenge to someone who struggles with socialising.

Close environments like school where having friends and socialising are a must. They are hard too.

Parts of my life that have been smoother follow this social model of disability. I did not get any 'better' (medical model), but the life around me matched up more with what I could join in with: college, university.

Things I did not think were autism, that I came back to live at home (lots of us do – but why did I, was it because I did not have a house load of friend[s] to move in with?), that I have never managed to sensibly feed myself (surely this is just scattiness?) all tick boxes in the pre-mapped parts of this landscape.

The having of close long-lasting relationships could be the next mountain in this uncharted land.

In parts, autism is an asset. It makes me sexually open minded. I can be very pragmatic, I understand the transactional nature of dating, I can move on when things are over. I am loyal. The tendency towards obsession means I learn furiously about my partners, becoming the resident expert in them. Which is charming for the first year, lovely for the second, a little unnerving for the third and unbearable for the fourth.

I am great at relationships that last around two years. Beyond that...

Well, I am wandering around in the uncharted territories hoping not to bump into dragons.

14.5 I can't keep up

I have seen children with autism get so frustrated about not being able to have something they want that they lose control.

I have seen them want to join in with a game, or conversation, but not be able to follow the instructions that are the route to inclusion.

I talk about different parts of the spectrum, in my last post I speculated about the different landscape here. Now I am wondering if the contours are the same, but experienced at different levels.

My partner tries to talk to me about a very touchy subject.

I follow the words, but my emotions do not keep pace. And although I understand the words, my emotions do precisely what those children's emotions do.

I sense danger. I feel attacked. I lash out. I do not mean to. I can unknit all my words and explain how they are not cruel. But I know I said them all to defend. Like an animal caught in a trap biting at people who try to help it escape.

And then it escalates as the two parts of the conversation – the meaning in the words, and the emotions – become further and further out of sync.

He hears the meaning in my words, and his emotions keep pace, and he comes back, and I hear in his response all the terrible things I have said in my panic. (Or not so terrible with the un-knitting.) And ... well ... that does not fix anything.

I understand language. I process it. I use it. I am not like those people at the other end of the spectrum from me. No, I am not like them at all. Things are different at this end. Totally different.

Or perhaps they are the same: acting as a ceiling on where we can join in. Their ceiling is placed low, they crash into it as they reach for a toy, or try to join in a social event. Mine is higher, I can get the toys, I can join in, I make friends, and now I smash into it here, where someone else's heart and life are at stake.

My experiences run parallel to those described by Jeremey in pop out box 22: 'I think being autistic is challenging my relationship'.

28

Language and autism

Dr Lila Kossyvaki, lecturer in Severe, Profound and Multiple Learning Disabilities in the Department of Disability, Inclusion and Special Needs (DISN) at the School of Education, Birmingham University, and member of the Autism Centre for Education and Research (ACER)

Several autistic individuals have attested that they had not seen the need to communicate using speech until their middle childhood although they could understand language much earlier.[213-214] It is also often reported that highly verbal adults with autism still often revert to limited speech patterns (e.g., one-word sentences) when experiencing negative emotions such as upset, frustration and stress. [213,215]

Current research has shown that language in autism is often delayed, but not deviant and that language development trajectories show great individual variability.[216] Delays have been reported in both the production of language (expressive language) and understanding of it (receptive language). Evidence is inconclusive as to whether expressive or receptive language is more affected in autism; some studies have reported more difficulties in receptive language,[217-218] whereas others have found that expressive language is more problematic.[219] Finally, there are also studies which have reported that difficulties in receptive and expressive language [occur] equally often.[220-221]

Research on language processing among individuals with autism is also inconclusive and hence only tentative conclusions can be drawn. Sahyoun et al.[222] have identified no language processing difficulties in individuals with autism at tasks with a visual component whereas Vulchanova et al.[223] have reported different processing patterns when compared with typically developing peers at the interpretation of figurative language (e.g. idioms, metaphors, jokes and indirect requests). Venker[224] found that difficulties with visual disengagement are likely to impact negatively on language processing while Eigsti et al.[225] claimed that even highly verbal individuals with autism are likely to find some aspects of communication, such as pragmatic language skills (e.g. turn taking), non-verbal communication (e.g. gestures, facial expression) and prosody, challenging. It has to be noted here that although deficits in language development was one of the diagnostic criteria for autism when the condition first appeared in the *Diagnostic and Statistical Manual III*,[226] this has been removed from the most recent *Diagnostic and Statistical Manual V*.[227] This change possibly reflects the view that people with autism might not have difficulties with language per se but with the use of language in social situations or/and different perceptual/attentional patterns.

A number of interventions widely used with children with autism prompt adults who work with this population to use minimal speech, wait for initiations and give them time to process information.[228] Several studies have shown so far the benefits for individuals with autism when neurotypical people adopt a minimal language approach. Potter and Whittaker[229] explored the connection between minimal speech and spontaneous communication and found that when school staff adopted a minimal speech approach, the children increased their spontaneous communication. Similarly, Ingersoll[230] trained adults to use simplified language and this spurred more initiations by children with autism. Other studies have focused on the element of slowing down and giving people with autism time to process information and initiate communication. McAteer and Wilkinson[231] trained school staff in a 'facilitative style of interaction' and one of the principles they asked staff to follow was to wait for the child to start communication. Gillett and LeBlanc[232] trained mothers of children with autism in an approach to increase their children's language and play and found that the component the mothers had more difficulties in was waiting for initiations. In a similar vein, Kossyvaki et al.[233] developed with school staff an Adult Interactive Style Intervention (AISI) to support spontaneous communication among children with autism. Use of minimal speech, waiting for the child to initiate communication and give them time to process the given information were some of the AISI's principles. The results of the study[233] showed that all members of staff increased the three principles considerably post intervention. Also, all children who participated in the study increased their spontaneous communication significantly after staff started using AISI.[234]

14.6 I make up stories

I have worked supporting teenagers with autism, before I knew that I was a part of their tribe.

I was amazed by the power of social stories. These are short, fact-filled narratives that explain upcoming events.

One young man I worked with could not cope with change of any kind, even something simple like a different poster on the wall would send him into a catastrophic meltdown.

This young man's family were struggling to cope and social services agreed to provide care for him once a week so they could rest and connect with each other. It was my job to tell him that on Friday he was not going home to his home, to his family, to the house he had slept in every night since he was born. Instead, he was going to a place he had never seen to stay with people he did not know. I was provided with a social story to use to give him this information.

The sheer quantity of change the social worker was expecting him to cope with was ridiculous. I remember laughing about it with colleagues. How naïve she was. She had no idea what he was like. It would not work.

But we duly read the social story we [had] been given, twice a day for a week. On Friday he arrived announcing that today he would go home to a different house and sleep in a different bed. He got on the bus without fuss. He had a great time.

I was stunned.

The power of stories.

I cope with change. My life is in a constant state of flux. I am not *that* autistic ... or am I?

I noticed something this week:

I make up stories.

Constantly, I create narratives in my head about what is happening next in the immediate and in the long-term. I create my own calm through these stories.

(*These narratives are my equivalent of the Now and Next boards Dawn writes about in pop out box 36: 'Exploring student shut-down'. I have, in my time, known students who were unable to take part in the present unless they knew what was coming next, their Now and Next boards were essential for them to feel safe in the present moment.*)

Thinking about it, my need to create stories is more noticeable when I am going into a situation without knowing about it. When I was dating my first husband, he arranged an extremely romantic surprise meal, and would not give me a single clue as to where we were going as he drove me there. I was horrid to him in return. He sprang an even bigger surprise on me later in our relationship, taking me by helicopter to a beach we had seen in a painting to propose to me with a ring he had designed and had made himself. My response was fear.

If you tie my hands, so that I cannot write these stories, I cannot go through life as a 'normal' person, I become very 'autistic'.

Why did I notice this now?

Well, because some stories have to be co-created. When you are forming a partnership, looking at a future, the stories must be co-authored. I am still trying to write them, but my partner is refusing to hold the pen, he is writing a different story. He writes one with me in, but it is not my story. He is erasing what I write.

It is frightening to realise how fragile you are underneath. I do a good job. I have a child. I pass in the world as neurotypical. I cope. I am fine. I can be happy. Take away the stories and there is so much to fall down and break.

14.7 Ticking the right boxes

At the start of this year, I took myself to my local GP, and without looking at anything apart from his desk carefully said aloud the sentences I had practised.

The ones that said I thought I had autism.

I was given a succession of check-box lists, I checked the boxes.

Did I fail or pass those tests? There's the black and white thinking I have grown quite fond of in the months since.

In my mind I failed them. The boxes I checked showed me up as such and such a percent this, or such and such a percent that. Failing the first one meant I got presented with the next one, which I again duly failed.

And so began a journey to diagnosis. And when I got that diagnosis, I started this blog, as you know.

But this week I went back.

I was told when I received my diagnosis that a number of services were open to me. One of which was a counselling service that someone close to me strongly encouraged me to take.

This week I went to my first counselling session. A little tentatively. Would I be told I was not coping? That I was not thinking straight? That my understanding of the situation was slightly skewed? So much of getting diagnosed has been discovering my own fallibility.

One of the first questions I was asked was whether there had been any changes in my life since diagnosis. I reported the easy to say ones first: that I feel liberated, that I have [been] able to be more myself, that life seems a little easier. And then the one that I knew would shock: that my relationship of 6 years has ended. The father of my child has moved out. Life is VERY different.

Out came the checklists. I checked boxes. I scored 5 out of a possible 36, and then on another one, a similar score [of] 4 out of a possible 28.

"Considering your circumstances, you are coping remarkably well, you seem fine."

Low scores were good. High scores would have been bad.

I can go back if I ever need them. But understanding myself better through the diagnosis process has led me to value myself more and to be able to think more clearly about what I want.

In many ways this feels like the end to a story. All the questioning at the start of the process, and now being known to myself and to others, and being okay, being fine, actually being pretty damned good.

I am keen to find other blogs about people who have taken this journey too. If you know any, do share them with me.

I will keep tweeting but I am slowing the blogging down.

14.8 Just out of reach

Sometimes when things are just out of reach, it is harder to understand and accept than when things are way way out of reach.

In a rescue situation the difference between the rope falling a few millimetres out of your grasp or a few miles means nothing. Out of reach is out of reach.

In the world around me I see examples of people with Autism for whom a close relationship with a significant other seems miles out of reach. Perhaps it feels so out of reach for them that they do not even try.

For me it is just millimetres out of reach, I almost have all the skills, I almost understand the communication required, I so nearly get it right. But I miss.

The scary thing about my situation is [that] no one sees a need here. Unlike the rescue analogy where the rescuer would realise the rope had not been grasped and would throw again, because I seem to be okay there is no help. Rescuers vanish.

To switch analogies: TV talent shows. The difference between the ones that can sing, those that cannot, and those that can but lack a certain something which is the difference which could one day make them a star is critical. Those that cannot sing get told so. They go home, lick their wounds and, if they are wise, try something different, or go and learn to sing.

It is harder for the ones that can sing but lack the some-thing. They stand around feeling as if the world is unfair. In their minds they did the same as the person who became a star but they were not similarly rewarded. They expect their family members, their nearest and dearests to make the sacrifices necessary for them to become a star. Their partner works to pay the rent whilst they rehearse waiting for a stardom that will never come. They appear so similar to those that are successful, but actually they are more similar to those who failed outright.

Perhaps this is what I need to recognise myself. I should stop thinking I have understood it all, and start realising that maybe I need more help, or need to aim for something different.

I often wonder whether the love that I am perusing is a neurotypical model of love.

Maybe I should work out what an autistic love would look like and aim for that.

15   Reflection: history repeating

In the aftermath of our relationship, we worked cooperatively to separate our finances, to share the material things we owned together and to plan how we would co-parent. We continued to misunderstand each other and clash, but year on year we do better. Our son has no memories of living with Mummy *and* Daddy. Without wasting our energy on fighting with each other, we have both had more to give him and he has thrived, his time is split equally between us.

Fearing for my future, my mother warned me not to make up stories. She told me not to plan any new relationships, to simply wait and see what time brought my way. But unable to move through time without the guidance of a story I ignored her advice.

I decided that diagnosis would be the thing that would make the difference. Because I was diagnosed, and knew I was autistic, the next time I tried to be with someone it would be different. I began a relationship with an old friend, someone I had known for more than 20 years. We lived 300 miles apart. (Just as I lived 300 miles apart from my first husband and we met, and just as I lived 300 miles apart from my son's father when he and I met. Yes, this time things were definitely different!)

My friend and I got married.

We remained living 300 miles apart.

My mother and my sister both gently advised me to stay living separately from my husband. But all the stories I have learned about relationships have the couple living together, and so the stories I made up all involved him living under the same roof as me. My son's father spotted the pattern between himself and my ex-husband and my new husband and gave me the same warning as my mother and sister.

But my mind is a fierce instrument, and in it I was right and they were wrong. This time it *would* be different. This time we both understood I was autistic. We planned the move to be a slow transition, occurring over 18 months to allow me to adjust.

Optimistically I began a small photoblog, this time it was not hidden away online anonymously. I published it on a social media account I use for work that had at that time more than 4000 followers and I shared it across other social media platforms, bringing the numbers of people seeing it closer to 25,000. My name was on it. It was my private life, my autism, very publicly on display, because this time it was going to be different.

I planned to honestly chart the hurdles we would face as we conducted a relationship across a neurodivergent divide. Believing that ultimately it would document how they were surmounted, and how we got to the happily-ever-afters at the end of my made-up stories.

I did not see the echoes of the past until I pasted the words from that photo album into the following chapter (16) and began to edit them for publication. I am sure you will spot them far quicker than I did.

I wrote the photoblog posts four years after writing the original anonymous blog, and yet in places they are almost word for word the same. I wrote them thinking I was discovering something new, when really, I was once again repeating the past and risking someone else's heart as I did so.

Getting diagnosed does not change the fact that I am autistic. I am still worn out by continuous social contact. I still fixate on small things and think of myself as petty. I still narrate my own binary thinking to myself, ironically judging its rightness or wrongness. I still wrestle between trying to control how my husband positions things in the house and not building him a cage out of all my many rules. I still misunderstand communication and believe that what I know and think is known and thought by everyone.

Knowing that I do all of these things has not stopped me from doing any of them. Editing Chapter 14: Blog part three, was chilling for me. I am pregnant with my second child. Will this small potential person get to grow up with a Mummy *and* a Daddy, or will I find myself in the future working out the details of a three-way co-parenting arrangement?

You can see in the posts my plan not to be autistic when he moves in. The same plan I had at 11 years old. Thirty years of life and I have not developed a new version of my 'how to be okay in the future' narrative. I expend huge amounts of energy trying not to be me. Not accepting the reality of my own mind.

29

Neurodiversity

Neurodiversity is a term first coined by Singer[235] to represent brain differences in an equivalent way to biological differences: biodiversity is to the body what neurodiversity is to the mind. Biodiversity is recognised as positive, a necessary and useful part of an evolving species. Neurodiversity signals having different brain types to be similarly positive and productive as we progress as a species.

I called my online photoblog 'Love across a neurodiverse divide'. My use of the word neurodiverse, and the words neurodiversity and neurodivergence, within that blog signal a movement in my understanding of autism. No longer am I fixed on working out whether it is a disability or a difference, I am beginning to recognise that, certainly in terms of how I was considering these options, it can be both.

An autistic brain is definitely different to a neurotypical brain, be that physically (see pop out boxes 3: 'Physical differences and research bias' and 5: 'Genetic differences and research bias') or be that in terms of the lived experience of the person possessing that brain. The difference is not up for debate. The bit

we debate is whether that difference equates to a disability or not, and that is where my binary thinking mind got stuck for so long.

In truth all brains are different. If you could up sticks from your own brain and settle down in someone else's for a week or two, you would find aspects of that other brain that worked better than yours and aspects that did not work as well. Some experiences of difference are disabling, others are enabling. It is not a clear-cut thing.

Steve Silberman, author of the award-winning book *NeuroTribes*[36] which documents the history of neurodiversity explains neurodiversity (p. 17) as being:

the notion that conditions like autism, dyslexia, and attention-deficit/hyperactivity disorder (ADHD) should be regarded as naturally occurring cognitive variations with distinctive strengths that have contributed to the evolution of technology and culture rather than mere checklists of deficits and dysfunctions.

Walker[236] writing for the autistic people's organisation Autistic UK CIC, which aims to promote and protect the civil and human rights of the autistic population and campaigns for change to enforce those rights, increase understanding and improve services, argues (paras 3–5) that neurodiversity is an essential form of human diversity:

The idea that there is one "normal" or "healthy" type of brain or mind or one "right" style of neurocognitive functioning, is no more valid than the idea that there is one "normal" or "right" gender, race or culture.

The classification of neurodivergence (e.g. autism, ADHD, dyslexia, bipolarity) as medical/psychiatric pathology has no valid scientific basis, and instead reflects cultural prejudice and oppresses those label[l]ed as such.

The social dynamics around neurodiversity are similar to the dynamics that manifest around other forms of human diversity. These dynamics include unequal distribution of social power; conversely, when embraced, diversity can act as a source of creative potential.

Or put simply, as the sticker of a rainbow infinity symbol that I purchased during the writing of this book says: "Neurodiversity is biological fact."

16 Love across a neurodiverse divide (explanations of a photoblog)

This chapter contains the explanations I wrote for the photoblog that I set up to chart what I presumed would be the hurdles my partner and I would overcome in our neurodiverse love affair. The titles of each section describe the image in the photo that accompanied each post as it was published online.

16.1 An empty space on brand new shelves

To live together a great many things must change. One of the most obvious is that our possessions will be under one roof.

Change is often difficult for people.

Change can be particularly difficult for autistic people.

This is well known.

But the whys are less thought about.

For me, the way things are in my house is not an accident, they have been considered, they are set up just so – even the mess. And they all interrelate. I see this interrelation when I am not coping so well; if my mental health dips, then there are more dishes unwashed on the side, if I am stressed, then the work resources are disorganised.

If there were suddenly to be more dishes on the side, this causal relationship would work in reverse: the dishes would make me unwell.

Things need to be the way they are in order for life to be okay ... clearly articulating this I can see it is not true ... but this is a feeling, not a thought.

Sudden change can be traumatic.

We first discussed moving in together two years ago. I realised his stuff would need come with him, so I had shelving commissioned.

I got used to there being shelves in the house.

Over the past eighteen months he has been bringing things to the house, putting *his* things away in *my* home.

We are nearly there – there is only one space left.

Up until four spaces ago I felt nothing but panic when I saw this accumulation of stuff.

But currently it has a nice weight to it, a steadying effect.

I am ready for this part of the change.

It feels nice to be ready and to be able to look forward to it ... I was going to say 'like a normal person'.

But the idea that neurotypical is normal and neurodivergent is abnormal is not true. Neurodiversity is normal.

What you can spot when I think something like that is that my measures of 'normal' are neurotypical ones.

I want to have the relationships I see: I have heard that people in love look forward to living together. Part of me wants to be the 'normal' I have heard about.

Craving a normal that does not describe you is not healthy. Creating a description of normal that includes everyone promotes health.

16.2 A door open, the same door pictured ajar and closed

One of these is wrong all year round.
One of these is right in winter.
One of these is right in summer.

180

Right and wrong.

Good and bad.

Safe or dangerous.

Binary thinking.

I think in these terms. Thinking in a binary way is typical of autism (that is not to say that all autistics will do this or that neurotypicals will not do this).

They interrelate. To do things the 'right' way is to be 'safe'.

My house is full of these tiny rules. You would not notice it were you to visit as I know that it is 'right' for visitors to be allowed to do as they please.

I did not used to have so many. Bad times in life tend to generate them. When you need to feel safe, you need more of them.

With my first husband we agreed on each thing as we went along. Much like any couple working out how to live together: which way up do the knives go on the draining board? Sharp end up so that muck drains to the handle, or sharp end down so it is safer to retrieve them? Which is right?

But ... there are a lot now. When my new husband moves in, I have a choice:

Teach him all of them.

Learn to let go of them.

With the standard couple narrative, the rights and wrongs are easy to guess – like it is wrong to leave wet towels on the floor and right to do the dishes.

But the rights and wrongs around here are in my head ... he would not be able to work them out.

He has said he will happily learn them all, but I am to forgive him if he is not as good at following them as me.

So I could list them all and teach him the ways of this house of rules.

But I love him.

I have no wish to cage him in this way.

So – if I can – I want to learn to let them go.

I am not sure how.

181

16.3 A screen shot of a WhatsApp message

The message read as follows.

Me: Let's go with WhatsApp messages instead.

Him: OK!

Me: Sorry if I was a bit off hand when you asked about the train. I didn't see what or why you wanted to know. It felt like you were asking questions for questions sake. Which is probably making friendly conversation. I like talking to you. Honestly.

Him: That's ok. I have to ask a couple of questions to see if you're in a talking mood. You weren't, so I stopped. :) I'm happy just having you there.

Me: Haha ... oh dear.

Him: So if you don't want to talk its fine.

Me: It felt like a monkey being made to dance. It is the answering questions. Rather than the being given information and commenting on stuff.

Him: But I have to figure out if you do or not.

Me: I know. I am not complaining. This is meant to be an apology for being offhand.

Him: No, but you're typing faster than me. It is taken as an apology! You don't have to apologise.

Me: I do not have to. I choose to.

At the point at which I switched our faltering communication from talking verbally to texting (even though we were sat next to each other), we had been watching television in silence for two hours. Unbeknownst to me he was perfectly happy. And unbeknownst to him I had spent the whole time quietly seething.

I had had a very long day. Being asked 'small talk' questions is something I find super difficult. They have no 'right' answer so I do not know what to say. If he had asked me about a big topic, or asked my opinion on something it would have been easier. But, "How was the train?" was both baffling and infuriating.

After a long day the last thing I want is to be made to dance the small talk dance by someone who is meant to be on my side.

Turns out he knows this, and was asking the questions to test the water.

Following this exchange, I went for a run with my best friend. In explaining it all to her, I said in exasperated tones: "If he wants to know if I am up for talking I would rather he just ask that!"

"So tell him," she replied.

Now he greets me with: "Chatty or not?"

Simple and to the point and very loving. I say yes, no, slow, or give me a moment. And it is easy.

16.4 A tablet mounted on an adjustable stand

Meet my husband.

We have been together for more than three years now, but we live 300 miles apart.

I find living with the people I love very difficult. (This is one of the things that flashes through my mind when people tell me I am "not very autistic".) Where other newlyweds might look forward to their first house together, I am very daunted.

We plan to try and live together soon. It is not just me who is daunted by this, close family and friends have cautioned me against it. Not because they disapprove of my choice of man but because they are frightened for me.

It is hard to talk about these things without sounding callous. So I will talk about something else instead:

When I was younger, I had a desktop computer that I used for word processing. One of those big chunky things. I am one of the Xennial generation, tech moved fast when I was young. I had a few games I could play on it, nothing too fancy.

Then my father bought me a copy of *Riven*. It was the first 3D immersive game I had seen. I loved it but the computer could not handle it. It crashed every time it tried to cope with something so big and so beautiful. Crashing rendered the computer useless, not only for playing the game but for everything else too.

Not wanting to live with my husband is not a rejection of him, it is an awareness that he is too big and beautiful for me to be able to process in full. When we have tried living together in the holidays, for a week or ten days, the most I have made it is around four days before becoming catatonic.

Unlike the game he is not all or nothing, I can have a manageable amount at a distance via video chat on a tablet supported by a wonderful tablet-holding-gadget.

16.5 Britney's shaven head

My Mum and my sister always say I never share a problem until it is over. And they are right.

Last week the upcoming changes got too much for me and I cut off half my hair. Not as dramatic as Britney but dramatic enough for me. My pigtails are half as long now.

I got too wound up to be able to tolerate the sensation of tying my hair up, so I had to make it lighter.

Sensory differences are not just to do with the difference in the initial registry of the sensation; background stimuli and background stressors can affect anyone's capacity to cope with stimulus.

I am fine now. I have had a nice new hair cut (something I think I have done three times in the past 14 years, once before getting married, once after getting divorced ... spotting a theme! I got married this time around without having a haircut ... that has to be a good sign).

16.6 An old desktop computer

You reboot a computer if it has gone wrong or you have installed new software or you want to update its thinking in some way.

I am beginning to wonder if my brain crashing shares a similar purpose.

I have gone from not being able to think of all the changes approaching without it feeling haunting and dreadful, to telling him to bring extra ramekins if he wants to.

It can take me longer to reach a 'normal' conclusion but once something clicks in my mind it stays there.

Just four days to go...

16.7 My reflection in a train vestibule window

He has moved in, and I am back at home on the rails.

In times of transition, spaces that remain the same, and predictably so, are a sanctuary.

And on particularly peopley days, train vestibules are rather lovely.

16.8 A single eye

At breakfast, I look up and he smiles at me, I quickly look back to my breakfast.

On the sofa, I look across at him and he looks at me. I shift my gaze back to the TV.

In the kitchen, in the dining room, passing on the stairs, his eyes search out mine, he looks at me and he smiles.

My world shrinks to the floor, my plate and the television.

He vanishes.

In my head I whisper: stop looking at me, I can't see you.

Then he plays his VR games, his eyes sealed inside a gadget, his arms swinging wildly and I see him and I am overjoyed that he is here.

But when he looks at me, I look away.

Eye contact is a strange game.

16.9 A packet of antibiotics

He has been living with me now for a few weeks. And I have been coping.

Initially, coping was a bit overwhelming. I confess to opening kitchen cupboards a few times and bursting into tears.

Imagine a nightmare where your house is suddenly not your house, it looks the same but everything has changed.

My rational mind knows that none of this should count as a real problem. But my brain does not have the flex required to just go with things as they change.

Of course, no one likes change and everyone in relationships has to compromise. I am not sure how to articulate the fundamental difference involved here in having an autistic brain over a neurotypical brain.

I *want* to flex, I understand the compromises and I think they are a great idea. But the flex just is not there. My brain is rigid and the only way it changes is by breaking and starting again with a new rule.

So that is what I have been doing. One by one I have encountered these blocks, from silly things like the salt being behind too many things in the cupboard to much bigger things to do with parenting my son.

Each time I have considered my old version smashed. I have made a plan for a new version and adopted a new rule. It has something of the feeling of trampling on all you have worked so hard to build. But it is a purposeful trampling because out of the ruins I intend to build a loving shared life.

And it has been working.

I have been coping.

I am not sure how I could have done it any better.

And of course, he has been fully supportive and understanding (he is unreasonably kind).

But.

On Sunday I spent the morning in hospital. First one and then a second as I was too complicated for the first to treat.

My body has the habit of contracting infections when I am stressed. And has consistently done so for a good 15 years.

Initially I argued with medics that the infections could not be caused by stress. It did not seem like a scientific conclusion, there had to be some other hidden cause. But the parallels are too neat. A good friend threatened to kill themselves, two days later I was in AE. A serious incident at work during the day, AE in the night.

I am so much better at taking care of myself than I was. At my worst I had ten infections in a year. At the moment the last time I had one was summer last year.

But it was always going to be stressful sharing space, and as much as we have both done everything to manage it. My body, it would seem, has tapped out.

No need to worry about me. The drugs are working. The husband is lovely. And yes, I will take it easy.

It is just a really clear example of how, for many autistics, emotions get mangled in the physical.

I have neurodivergent friends whose emotions effect their guts and bowels, or they get headaches or changes in their seizure activity.

Mind and body are not so separate.

I contracted a further seven infections during the time covered in this chapter.

16.10 A cartoon of stick men entitled 'Call a spade a spade'

There are definite perks to being in a neurodiverse relationship. One, once you get used to it, is my bluntness.

If I know and trust you, I will tell you exactly what I think, without dressing it up, and without much awareness of its effect. A brutal level of honesty.

Now if I am telling you that your nose does not suit your face, or your name sounds funny, then this is not so much of a perk. But that I will say things like that adds to the authenticity of the more favourable comments, as does their somewhat unusual nature.

I was going to say [that] the compliments I give are not standard in format, but I dislike the word compliment – it suggests effort to be nice, effort to impress, or to please. I am just being honest. And if I like something about you, if I am impressed by you, if I love you: I will tell you.

There is no wondering what I am thinking for him, no guessing as to what might be a problem (he can just read social media for that!). And there is no doubt about what I think of him.

I liked it so I put a ring on it.

16.11 Me five months pregnant wearing workout clothing

Having been together for four years, my husband moved in with me four months ago.

Autistics are famous for not coping well with change, but we put plans in place. The move was glacially slow, happening over an 18-month period.

When any couple get together, there is a settling in period, working out who does what, and how the laundry is going to be done, who has control of the remote. After the lumps and bumps of the start things settle down.

My husband is the most easygoing man on the planet, so we did not really have to contend with any of this. But as the months roll on, it gets harder for me, not easier.

It feels like the screaming white noise of tinnitus, and I am beginning not to be able to feel or see him through it. It used to be when I was away, I looked forward to spending time with him. Now I spend the same time picking over minutiae in my head trying to work out what we could change to make it easier.

I come up with practical things ... strange, daft, but significant to me practical things, like being able to see the wall on either side of this piece of furniture. Stand a pile of books or a lamp at either end and my ability to cope goes downhill fast.

As I would advise for other people, I put compensatory strategies in place. For me this is exercise. I cope better with life after a workout.

But the truth remains.

Living with the man I love is something I cope with.

I would love for it to be something I loved.

The plan is to get there eventually. But for me, autism means that this will be a long road.

Those watching from the outside might think it simple and think it already done. But my husband and I both appreciate how real the threat of separation is. We would not part relationship-wise, but we may need to not live together.

I would like my second son to be able to grow up under the same roof as his father, especially after having failed to manage that for my first son.

16.12 A crystal ball

In common with a lot of autistic people, my default state is to presume you know what I know.

A thing in my mind is known, therefore you know it too.

There are various tests, like the Three Mountains Experiment,[1] the one with the police doll[2] and the Sally Anne Test[3] that are used in psychology to assess whether someone can put themselves in someone else's shoes.

I can do all of those tests. I can put myself in the other person's shoes. Because I have encountered the tests before, I have learned the situation. And in many many other areas of life, decades of practice have made this true as well.

Of course, if I stop and think about it, I do not really think you have a crystal ball and can know everything in my head. But this does not change the fact that this is my default setting.

From time to time, examples of it pop up. Just now my husband came downstairs. I was by our pedal bin in the kitchen, pressing the foot pedal repeatedly (I was trying to work out if the cat hair behind the bin was stuck to the floor or not – yuck – without touching it). My husband did something funny with his hair. I wondered: what are you doing, as I looked at him. He smiled at me and I said, "I am trying to see if it is stuck." He then looked affectionately bemused – a look I get a lot.

I had both assumed he was thinking, "What are you doing?" because that is what I was thinking. And assumed he knew there was cat hair on the floor that might be stuck or not. Because I knew that.

In unrehearsed situations I still assume everyone thinks like me and knows what I know. The incident above was amusing, we had another a few weeks back in which the missing information was the amount of money I had in a particular bank account in association with a large and unexpected bill we had just received. That conversation was more tense, and my assumption that he knew how much money was in my bank account did not help.

190

I got frustrated in that conversation because it felt, to me, like he was being awkward, when actually the problem was the missing piece of information from our conversation. It may have seemed to him that I was being awkward too and withholding the information. When in truth I did not realise it was missing, because it was known to me.

17 Reflection: interoception

At the start of this book, I explained that my intentions for neatness, clarity and objectivity in my reporting of experience ultimately failed. Although the failures are many, the turning point for me was Chapter 13, the point at which I realised that my past is in my present. From here on in, I am just presenting you with what I have got. Here is what I know. I am no better positioned to work out what it means than you are. If anything, you are better placed. This chapter begins just before I got married for the second time and explores the impact of interoception on my relationships. The subsequent chapters (Chapter 18 to Chapter 20) tell you about my emotional landscape, my pregnancy and my special interest.

17.1 Are you excited?

My husband and I planned a relatively small wedding: 50 or so friends and family would see us wed in the old town hall near to my home. We would go from the town hall to a friend's field where food would be served, a fire lit and there would be singing and dancing.

The little town hall is so old and fragile that it is only opened for weddings. Its internal decoration has the stately frailty of an elderly woman wearing fine her Sunday best. Wedding gifts were originally intended to help the bride and groom set up house, they were tea towels, irons, cups and plates. Marrying just before turning 40, and each with a house and furniture of our own, we did not feel we needed gifts, so instead guests were tasked with bringing wild flowers and wine. The idea being that we would share the wine at the reception and the wild flowers would be placed in vases around the town hall to bring it to life a little.

I have a vase I bought with my pocket money in Spain when I was very young, and another inherited from my Grandma that always stood in her living room, and a jug from a great-grandmother. These vases of sentimental value were to be the vases that held the wild flowers, connecting us in our present day to people no longer with us. My husband's idea of sentimental differed somewhat and in the weeks running up to the wedding he perfected his glass-cutting skills, crafting much-loved spirit bottles into vases.

The day before the wedding everything was done, there were no last-minute jobs, no catastrophes, nothing that needed frantic-ally doing. We were allowed to go into the venue to 'set up'. We did not really have anything to 'set up', so together my husband and I took the opportunity to go and walk around the space that would, the following day, be where we became husband and wife. We took with us the vases to place on windowsills and tables as we wandered about the little hall.

In the weeks leading up to the wedding, people from different walks of my life had all been asking me the same question: "Are you excited?" I initially found this irksome. The question grew more irritating the more I was asked it.
I even got an email from my sister with the title "Are you excited?" and NO CONTENT AT ALL. I was furious.

Eventually I reached such a level of seething that my husband took it upon himself to warn family and friends not to ask.

I was so offended by the question, I was sure it must represent some kind of personal insult. I fished around for what the insult could be. At the time my explanations were many:

"Do they think just because I am marrying you, I am going to turn into some ditsy woman who only cares about chair covers and seating plans?""Do they think I do not care about my work just because I am going to wear a white dress on one day?"

I was working until six days before the wedding, at which point I would have a venue, a frock, and the catering; anything else was to be dealt with in those six days.

In those six days we decorated the field that the reception would be held in with handmade bunting. We asked friends at dinner to shell the dried Honesty seedpods to be used as confetti. We made paper cups out of recycled bridal magazines I had been given to hold the confetti. Essentially, we played at weddings for the week, there was nothing that needed doing. It was only as we were putting out the vases on the final day before the wedding, that I realised why the "Are you excited?" question was so annoying.

In the quiet of the hall, moving around positioning the much-loved vases with my husband in the spring sunlight was very peaceful. And yet my heart thumped in my chest. I was puzzled. I do not normally recognise or feel my heartbeat, I would only notice it if I had been working out hard, or if I was really frightened.

I looked at the vase in my hand – it was not heavy – I looked back across the room to the flight of three stone steps we had climbed to get into the room, they hardly represented a work out. I considered whether something had frightened me. Could I be ill?

I looked across the room at my gentle husband,

"I think..." I said.

He looked up at me,

"...that I am excited."

"Yes," he smiled, "you are."

The question had annoyed me because I did not know the answer, and everyone expected me to know.

Imagine yourself to be a person who always struggled at maths. Then imagine you hit a period of time in your life where everyone you met felt it perfectly acceptable to ask you difficult maths problems, and expect immediate answers. They thought it right and proper to do this in public. And it happened at work, in your private life, even strangers in shops might ask you if you happened to purchase particular items.

No one likes having their weaknesses publicly revealed.

Knowing how I feel is tricky for me. My interoceptive system, the sensory system that senses your internal feelings (like the quickening of your heartbeat or the fluttering of butterflies in your stomach) does not work as well as another person's might. We are used to the idea of impairment in some of the well-known senses. Most people understand that a person can be blind, or partially sighted, that they might be long- or short-sighted or may experience other sight difficulties such as cloudy vision or tunnel vision. We know, generally, that there is a broad spectrum of abilities with regard to our sense of sight. The same is true for other senses, and impaired interoception would seem to be a relatively common experience for autistic people.

Researchers have noted deficits and differences in interoceptive processing in autistics.[237-244]

17.2 Smiling at work

A different day gave a different example of interoception at play. This was a work day: a brilliant day.

To say I love my job is somewhat of an understatement. I give it my all and often end up at the end of the day completely spent in a wonderful way.

To do my job, I travel around the country on trains and on this particular day I had caught the train to my husband's house after work. He was, at that time, used to me arriving shattered and unable to string a sentence together. We had a wonderful routine which involved me sitting on his huge comfortable chunky corduroy sofa and watching dreadful television programmes, and him feeding me salt and vinegar crisps so strong they make your eyes water with a mixed salad and a stiff drink: my idea of heaven.

After taking his dog for a walk, he joined me on the sofa, rolling his eyes at my choice of television programme. I had been sitting there for a while. My fingers were hooked into my cheeks on both sides. I had not realised I was doing this. When I looked across at him as he sat down, I noticed that my elbows lifted off the sofa, something they do not usually do when I turn my head.

He looked at me, and we both realised at the same time what I was doing: I was clawing at my face on both sides with my hands.

He laughed affectionately at me, raising his eyebrows.

"Okay...," he said, "what are you doing?"

I took my hands away and inspected my clawed fingers. "My face is too high up," I replied, putting my hands back and trying to lower my cheeks by hooking my fingers into them and pulling them down.

This suddenly seemed ridiculous and we both laughed helplessly. This did not help with the height of my cheeks!

I had had such a good day I had smiled all day (without realising it) and I had reached the point where the muscles in my face were hurting from the smiling. But I did not know I was happy.

Some days I notice how I am feeling when I pick up on a facial expression in the mirror. I will look at myself in the bathroom mirror when I am brushing my teeth or brushing my hair and think, "goodness you look tired/sad/worried", but often I do not notice and do not feel a particular need to know.

Of course, if I did have a better awareness of my changing mood when it began to change in a dangerous direction, I could do something to amend that before it reached a crisis point.

I ought to monitor my emotional state consciously throughout the day as an act of personal responsibility. I feel towards that act of personal responsibility in much the same way we all feel when first presented with acts of personal responsibility. Teaching children to brush their teeth is a prime example; no child responds with: "Ah brilliant, I get to clean my teeth, let me at this task!" They are cajoled, prompted and eventually habituated into doing it. Two-year-olds are known for their defiant nature, and their tendency to kick back against such social pressures. From personal experience I can report that 40-year-olds are far worse. You cannot make me do it and I will not do it. I know it is good for me, but so what? My inner toddler is a force to be reckoned with.

17.3 How are you?

A common piece of small talk is for someone to ask you how you are. When you consider this question, it is massive. How are you? How are you feeling, how are you physically, where are you in your head, what are you worrying about, what are you hoping for, how is the very essence of your self doing at this moment in time? *How are you*?

I am always surprised when people ask it. It seems like such a big request. I am especially surprised when people I do not know that well ask it. Are they requesting such intimacy with me? Or do they have the audacity to think that my soul, my self, my 'I' is just theirs for the asking?

Of course, I am also not surprised. I know that this is a thing. People ask this question, but they do not want the answer. They want, "I am fine, how are you?" or "Could be better, how's things with you?" There is a set of standard replies and in most situations, I can be trusted to give them.

But at home, with my husband, or with good friends it is different.

Recently a set of close friends video called us so that we could all have dinner together in the virtual world. As the connection clicked through and they appeared on the screen of the laptop on our dinner table, the conversation was opened with a "Hey! How are you?" To which I replied, "Blimey, starting with big questions!" My friends laughed and the question was retracted.

With my close friends I can reply as I think. With most of the world I avoid doing so.

Sometimes my husband will ask me, "How are you?" He knows what he is doing when he asks this question. Sometimes he will unleash with these three simple words an account that lasts over an hour in the telling, but this is rare. More often he asks when he senses I do not know the answer. Sometimes I can say, "not good" but I have nothing left in explanation after that. Most often I answer with: "I do not know."

There are two types of "I do not know" answer. The first is usually a good sign: "I do not know, do you really want me to think about it?" This means that I have no idea how I am, but my mind is occupied with another task and I am not keen to switch it to the task of assessing my inner state. The second type is more worrying, and there is a blank facial expression of dim recognition that goes with it. I look up at him expressionless save for my eyes being a little frightened by the realisation of my own answer: "I do not know."

That second response: I do not know – I do not know how I am, I am lost to myself, I cannot find out, I am worried that my 'I' has wandered off somewhere and is not safe, is sometimes followed by me repeating the question after my answer: "I do not know, how am I?" And then he will answer.

It is far more common for my husband to *tell me* how I am than for me to tell him how I am. Initially this was a strange conversation, one that was prompted by my wide-eyed slightly panicked asking. He would say things like: "I do not know, I am not in your head," and I had to push him for an opinion.

Later on, with a little figuring out between us he became more confident, because he does know. Or at least he will know enough to give me the bones of it, the framework, some sort of structure that I can comprehend and then I fill in the gaps, or the gaps are less worrisome.

How can he know?

Well, he knows the comings and goings of my life so he can make reasonable predictions based on events and the amount of sleep I have had. He can also read my body language and recognises facial expressions that he has seen before at similar times. I have a particular blank look that usually prompts the "How are you?" "I do not know, how am I?" routine, so in a way he knows the answer before he asks, because the answer is what made him ask.

17.4 Interoception

When my husband tells me how I am, in addition to his historical knowledge of my wellbeing and ability to read facial expressions, he may also be using his own interoception. We often joke between us that I am surprisingly autistic (surprising because I mask well) and he is surprisingly neurotypical (surprising because to his mind, he is in the middle of everything, he does not consider himself to be a man of extremes, but he seems very neurotypical to me).

Broad brushstrokes rarely serve anyone well, but sometimes they can help us get to a picture behind them so long as those observing recognise that the broadness is always inaccurate. In broad brushstroke terms, autistic people have poor interoception and neurotypical people have good interoception. There will be wild amounts of variety within the two, of course.

If you have good interoception, you can feel your own feelings well. It is like having 20:20 vision but for your own feelings. If you have poor interoception, as I do, it is like being partially sighted towards your own feelings. Just as a partially sighted person might only recognise a dark shape against a bright background, so I will only notice big bold emotions against a blank canvas background – like noticing I felt excited in the calm of the town hall.

Some people have been found to have exceptional interoception. I have my husband pegged as one of those people, but this is likely to be the bias of someone in love speaking. People with exceptional interoception can use their interoception to tap into the feelings of others. How?

When you walk down the street with someone it is likely that you will fall into step with them, stepping as they step. Our bodies have many ways in which they synchronise with the bodies around us and through that synchronicity we can gain insight into the feelings of another. We can see the same response in animals: if someone who has a pet dog, for example, walks in from work stressed, the dog will respond in a different way than if they walk in from work relaxed. Our mood is signalled by far more than our facial expressions and what we say. It is there in the tension in our muscles, the pallor of our face, our breath, our heart rate and so on.

Someone with superb interoception knows how they feel, and they can feel the change in their feelings in response to the presence of someone else's feelings. So, say they had been feeling calm and buoyant and someone entered the room who was stressed, breathing heavily, muscles tense, etc. Our superb interoceptor might notice an increase in their own breath rate in response to that person's and a tightening in their own muscles; they feel, in part, what the other person is feeling.

I believe I can lie in bed in the dark, not touching my husband, and as he lies beside me, he probably has a better idea of what I am feeling than I do. With another person this could be an alarming feeling – someone knowing more about you than you do is a form of vulnerability – but more than anything else I feel towards him, I trust my husband, so I can tolerate my ignorance with him.

Having someone tell me how I am helps me to respond to emotional cues in my life. For example, in the past, if I had been getting stressed by work, I would only have noticed at the point of collapse. Now if I am told, "You seem stressed" or "You seem tired" a few too many times, I will look at my to-do list which always sits alongside my computer and wonder if I should archive a few items until I am in a better position to manage them.

I have always known that sleep is essential for my sanity. In addition to sleep, my husband's observations have taught me other things that have a positive effect on my wellbeing. Knowing their effectiveness, I have been able to schedule these activities into my life more frequently, or at least protect them from being struck off the list at times of crisis.

You would never think to tell someone how they feel. It would seem like a strange overstepping of a mark. Why would you tell someone something that they already know, it is their feelings, of course they feel their feelings. But with someone like me, that *of course* is not true. I have feelings. But my ability to sense them is dulled. Getting told what those feelings are is useful to me.

If I were a more responsible person, I would recognise the truth in the paragraph above and take on trying to monitor my feelings myself. I should look in the mirror when I go to the bathroom and assess my facial expression. I should check the tension in my muscles; how high up are my shoulders? I should think about what food I am reaching for and why. If I cannot monitor my feelings internally, I should monitor my feelings from the external cues as others do. I should... But I do not.

I am sometimes asked if I would have wanted to have been diagnosed earlier. It is a tricky question. I am content with my life as it is, and the bad bits, such as there have been, have all contributed to my now, and I would not want to change that. An easier question to answer is if there were a 12-year-old girl who was like me, living now, what would I want for her? And with regard to this topic, I would want someone to support her in developing a habit for monitoring and recognising her emotions, because there are very real dangers in the not knowing.

17.5 An implausible world

Another aspect of life affected by altered interoception is the plausibility of the world around you. This might sound like a strange starting sentence but stick with me... Your feeling of your own feelings is instrumental to your sense of embodied self. You are a self, wandering around within a body. That body is not you, your 'youness' is something else, something harder to place.

From time to time, I play a small philosophical game with my son: he is five years old as I write, but we have played this game together in chats since he was three. I pretend to cut his finger off, and then I ask him where he is. Is he in his finger or is he in the rest of his body? As the game progresses, I chop off bigger and bigger portions of him. I realise in writing this that it sounds frightening, but it is played with many giggles on his part and it is very much understood to be imaginary, he does not think his mother is chopping him into increasingly smaller parts!

The game continues until he does not know where he is. He has given various answers through the years, certain that he is in his head, his heart, his stomach, or an area of space around his body but not entirely within his body. I have no real insight, but I like to think that his answers at different times in his life reflect a change in his awareness and development. Who knows, if I keep asking, he may one day be able to tell me where the self resides.

Wherever you are, you feel yourself to be in your body. Now consider yourself in a dream. In a dream you have a body and a self, and you move around within that dream. But something about it is less plausible, at some level you know it is a dream. If you know that it is not real life, then you will be liable to act differently. You might say ruder things, do riskier things, you might confront people you would not confront in life, or take part in sex acts you would never consider in real life. You might try to do things that go against the laws of nature, like jumping off cliffs or out of buildings in an attempt to fly.

A dream happens in your head, not in your body. Our bodies are, for the most part, paralysed by sleep to protect us, so that we do not run and leap off our beds or swing our arms wildly as we fight unseen foes or swim oceans.

In day-to-day life, our feelings connect us with our physicality. Your anxiety is the beating of your heart inside your ribcage, your nervousness is the churning of your stomach, your lust is heat in your loins, your embarrassment is a flush of warmth across your cheeks, your joy is the ache of the muscles pulling up your smile. All of these things let you know you reside in your body.

My heart will beat fast, my stomach will churn, my cheeks will flush, my muscles ache, but the connection, the tethering of those sensations to self is missing. In not feeling my feelings as profoundly as the next person might, I do not have as great a sense of embodiment as someone else does. This has positive, as well as negative, effects. My body does not pull my concentration away from a topic as it might were I more aware of it. My body does not interrupt the working of my mind and so I am able to focus at great lengths and think to great depths. But in not feeling embodied, I often encounter days which do not seem plausible.

I will look around at my house, at the faces of loved ones, and it's quite a mischievous feeling, a giggly silliness. They are not real. Nah … they are just, some sort of dream. This is not actually a day; it is a plaything. It is pretend.

And in those moments when life does not seem real, although I enjoy them a lot, there is risk. The risk that I would do all those things we do in dreams. In the main, I have been okay, my worst travesties of that boundary between the real and the unreal have been to speak a little too freely, a little too bluntly. I have not yet tried to leap from buildings, but I can see how someone who felt even less connection with reality could be tempted to do so.

Like everyone, I tend to believe people think like me. When the world loses its reality, I assume it has done the same for those around me. Sometimes I will lean in to my husband and whisper, "Does this seem real to you?" He looks surprised at the question. Why would I ask in such a mundane environment? We are not in a 3D cinema, we are not observing a hologram in an art gallery, why wouldn't the very ordinary, very real world seem real?

"Yes," he answers, bemused, "it seems real."

"Seriously?" I'll tease. I know he's pulling my leg, he is in on the joke. He knows it is not a *real* evening, that it is instead one of those pretend ones that pop up every so often to play with.

I recently read a study[32] that gave another clue to, not so much the unreality of life, but the disconnectedness from that reality that is often experienced by autistic people. The study focused on children, but it would seem reasonable to presume that if autistic children's brains are working in a particular way that they would continue to function in that way into adulthood, and so this might also give us an insight into the experience of autistic adults. The researchers found that autistic brains produced 42% more information at rest than neurotypical brains and speculated that this could lead to a more pronounced inner life.

If our inner worlds are somehow more real to us than the quieter inner worlds of neurotypical people, this would make sense in a small way of a seeming disconnect from the 'real' world. Although part of me wants to start a debate there about the nature of reality. My inner world is not unreal. In my inner world I do a lot of thinking about the outer world, and a good chunk of that is constructive, it helps me to interact in that outer world and it influences the outer world. But there is no need to start fights, so I will keep that chain of thought to myself.

The increased information produced by an autistic brain at rest, when compared to a neurotypical brain, could also be accounted for by the connection differences described in pop out box 3: 'Physical differences and research bias'.

18   Emotional connection

This chapter looks at autistic emotional connection through the lens of forming friendships and considers some of the ways in which autistic emotional processing can be different to neurotypical emotional processing.[1] The risks of understanding the autistic emotional landscape through neurotypical paradigms are highlighted by the collapse of my first marriage.

30

Autistic friendship

James Gordon, trustee of the London Autism Group Charity

Much of neurotypical friendship is built upon the social experience. A conversation between two or more people which can be made up on the spot. This may be on any random topic of popular culture with a selection of small talk thrown in. It may be in a crowded noisy environment which is difficult for an autistic person to filter out. For me, it is hard enough to maintain one conversation for very long, and also to concentrate for any length of time. To do so in a place full of distractions can be overwhelming, in which case an autistic person may seem to react strangely. We may

---

meltdown or shutdown (i.e. have a defensive fight or flight response).

A person with an executive functioning difference may become lost and unable to process the flow of conversation, thus finding it hard to contribute much in any group social outing. We frequently come across as awkward, as we find it difficult to process the flow of conversation on unfamiliar topics in the moment. In an attempt to compensate for this, some autistic people can miss out on rest and relaxation time, as they forensically examine past conversations and attempt to improve upon their performance. This often becomes a literal performance, in which a person will attempt to mimic neurotypical socialising in an attempt to fit in. This is known as 'masking' in the autistic community. We often need to come up with a script beforehand. Even if we prepare in this way, in a social setting a deviation from our expected script can derail our attempts to fit in. This can be exhausting for autistic people, increasing stress and leading to poor mental health.

When two people who are autistic meet and attempt friendship, often something different occurs.

For me, and many autistics, friendship comes from a shared sense of connection. This may be through an interest or a topic that fascinates us, which we feel confident to talk about. As autistic people, we frequently like to get straight to the point and so we socialise best by connecting through our interests. Friendships between autistic people can be much more relaxed and are in turn very refreshing. Having our opinions valued and respected can be a rare feeling for us. For this reason, we put a lot of value on our friendships. When autistic meets autistic, it can lead to some intense friendships that last a lifetime.

On the surface level, all friendships may appear to follow a set pattern, but there is also a lot going on underneath. I believe that the shared interests of autistic people allude to something far deeper. These connections we forge come from finding a sense of unity and from a shared sense of common identity. Common identity may be a familiar feeling for neurotypical people, but is much more uncommon for us autistics. Our search to feel comfortable in our own skin may end up being life-long, and finding autistic friends can feel like the fulfilment of that very human need.

18.1 Friendships and emotions

The vast majority of the relationships I have formed in adult life have been formed online. There is an idea that an online friendship is not real, purely because it is based in the virtual world. Whilst fraudulent relationships are possible online (as they are offline), this does not negate the reality of online relationships. Surely friendship is defined by things like respect and trust, more so than it is by whether these attitudes are displayed in a 'real' world or a virtual one.

I have met many of the friends I have made online, and in meeting them it does not feel like meeting a new person. Instead, it is like dropping by on an acquaintance from years ago. Indeed, in some meetings I have not realised that it was our first meeting, so well do I know them, their physical presence seems irrelevant. The realness of their body in space matters less to me than the realness of their thoughts and emotions which are themselves just as real online as they are offline.

Online you can quite literally read emotion. Someone will write and state, "I feel worried, I am upset, I am frightened." I read the words, I know what they mean, and I feel for that person. In life, if I had to rely on my own ability to notice changes in their facial expression and demeanour, perhaps I would not know so much.

My working life centres on the needs and abilities of people with profound and multiple learning disabilities. The focus my brain is

206

capable of has meant I have been able to take in information from research and real life about the life experiences of people with profound and multiple learning disabilities and become, in some regards, a specialist in the field. To this end, I deliver training days on topics that resonate with what I feel is important and the knowledge that I have.

One of the training days I offer is about the mental health needs of people with profound and multiple learning disabilities, needs that are often very acute and nearly always completely overlooked. I deliver that training day multiple times a year; if I look back over the past year, out of all of the training days I offer it is the one I have delivered most. The day has various interactive parts but it all hangs off a set of presentation slides, that are mostly there to remind me what to say and when. I say the same thing every time I do the day. As with much of my communication, it is planned, even the seemingly spontaneous parts are planned.

At one point in the day, I show a film that clearly displays where the vulnerability to mental ill health in this population might come from, and when the film has stopped playing, I highlight key points. Invariably as I highlight these points my voice cracks with emotion.

Recently someone sitting just to the side of me as I went over the points from the film approached me at the next tea break.

"How often have you played that clip," she asked.

"Oh, millions of times," I said.

"And do you cry every time?"

I laughed, "Yes, it is sad every time."

She had come up and asked because sitting so close she had seen the sheen come over my eyes as I forced the words out through potential tears. The words are planned, the tears are spontaneous, the emotion is always there, because I always care about the child in the film, and the children he represents, every single time I show it.

My emotions are permanent. The people I have loved I love still. I have been divorced; I have been through dramatic breakups. I have been heartbroken and lovelorn. The emotions do not die, do not change. I am baffled by people who say they hate their ex, or loathe them. I do not understand what their love could have meant. How is it possible to stop loving someone? Surely if you love then you love?

I am autistic and I am full of emotion, not emotionless. To have to defend this at all is bizarre.

One of the narratives that this idea of autistics being emotionless automata comes from is the old theory of mind one, where people are asked to place themselves in another's shoes. It is something, when tested, that autistics are not very good at. Only, when tested, it is always a neurotypical person's shoes they are asked to fill. I wonder how neurotypicals would fair if asked to stand in an autistic person's shoes? My own theory of mind is poor, but there is not a corresponding deficit for my empathy and compassion. Not being able to work out how a particular action or statement will come across to another is not the same as not caring about how you affect another.

The double empathy research (see pop out box 19: 'Double empathy research') shows that autistic people do not, as has long been said, lack empathy. Rather, they struggle to empathise with people who are not autistic. They tested people who are not autistic and they struggled to empathise with people who were autistic. Autistics empathised well with autistics. And neurotypicals empathised well with neurotypicals. When asked to empathise across the divide, if anything, autistics fared slightly better than neurotypicals as they have had more practice at it.

31

Autistic emotional processing and research bias

Research has shown that autistic brains process emotions differently to neurotypical brains, and autistic people deploy different emotional regulation strategies compared to neurotypical people.[40,134,245–256] Milton[3] points out that deficit models have become the dominant narratives in autism research. The research

into autistic emotional experience tends to interpret observed differences as deficits. It is also assumed that emotional regulation strategies, deemed as deficits, are an innate facet of autism rather than a learned, or culturally conditioned, state of affairs.

It is pertinent to question whether the pathologising of neurodiversity could lead to the "maladaptive" emotional regulation strategies reported by researchers[246,250,253,255] as being so prevalent amongst the autistic community. Even, as the researchers point out[40,134,245,253,256] amongst those they term as "high functioning" autistics (the preferred terminology within the autistic community is "low support needs").

- Could the overuse of self-blame observed by researchers[252] be a natural result of being brought up to believe that there was something wrong with you, rather than a natural result of a neurological difference?
- Would a person used to always having an adult monitor their behaviour be more inclined to vocalise in an attempt to gain help, as researchers observed of autistic participants,[253] than someone more accustomed to being permitted to operate independently?

Interestingly, the researchers[253] go on to note that "social support strategies (orienting and verbalizing to the experimenter) were ineffective for children with autism" (p. 1250). Why would this be?

- Are people more likely to dismiss the vocalisations of autistic children, to see them as less significant, less meaningful, because they are autistic? Or was it that the vocalisations were inaccurate in some way?

209

One also has to question whether the adaptive strategies recognised as effective emotional regulators within a neurotypical mind necessarily translate to an autistic mind. Rumination, for example[252] seems to fit very well with the focused nature of an autistic mind. The fact that a brain acts in a way that is counterproductive in one context does not automatically qualify that action as a deficit. In another context, this ability to focus becomes a strength. Surely neurotypical minds have similar two-sides-to-one-coin strengths and weaknesses?

Another topic worthy of consideration is whether research participants are being judged on their ability to successfully deploy neurotypical regulation strategies. Researchers[246] (p. 2139) remark on autistics being unable to use particular strategies even "when the technique was explained to them and when they were encouraged to use the strategy". They do not question whether there could exist effective *autistic* regulation strategies. McDonnell and Milton[257] (n.p.) point out that

> According to the accounts of people on the autism spectrum, the flow-like states brought about by the pursuit of 'special interests' or the repetition of actions can be seen as a necessary coping strategy for people and not 'behaviours' to be controlled or regulated.

Researchers[253] suggest possible differences between the appositeness of regulation strategies used by neurotypical and autistic people, noting that physically venting may actually regulate autistic children (whereas this is viewed as a maladaptive strategy in neurotypical children) and observing that having an adult nearby may serve to regulate neurotypical children, but will only do so for autistic children if it is a known and trusted adult.

We could also look to wonder whether the autistic people described as coping so poorly with their emotions within these studies might have had some of their pre-existing emotional regulation strategies removed? For example, many autistics report that stimming (repetitive actions or vocalisations) help them to self-soothe, and many 'treatments' for autism focus on blocking stimming.

Researchers observe autistic children as lacking "the desire to be comforted by a caregiver"[258] (cited by Glaser and Shaw[255] [p. 927]; an observation also made about me in 8.5), but what if that sentence were made a little longer: autistic children lack the desire to be comforted in the way that we would comfort a neurotypical child. With this extension you quickly get to the next question: how would an autistic child like to be comforted? Perhaps it is still true that they do not desire to be comforted, but that conclusion should not be drawn solely from observing a lack of conformity to a neurotypical norm.

Researchers admit that their insight into the emotional landscape of autism is in its infancy.[250] However it does seem that research is predominantly focused on the emotional differences of autistics as observed from the outside; i.e. it has focused on the areas in which autistic people do not act like neurotypical people. Very little research has been conducted on the reported autistic experience of emotional processing. I could not find research linked to the emotional shutdown so commonly reported by the autistic community, but that I was able to find so much that assumes neurotypical processing to be correct across the board says something in and of itself.

One area of overlap between reported autistic experience and the research world I did find was alexithymia.[134,245,248-249,259-261,263-264] Alexithymia is "a difficulty in understanding and expressing emotion words"[249] (p. 413) or simply lacking words for feelings.

Alexithymia is reported to be present in around 10% of the neurotypical population[265-266] and around 50% of the autistic population.[134,256,264] Researchers have wondered whether it is alexithymia, rather than autism, that accounts for some of the empathy deficits observed in autistic people.[249,261] See pop out box 19: 'Double empathy research' for further discussion of whether autistic people actually lack empathy.

My mother described feeling frustrated and helpless when, as a child, I would be clearly distressed and my mouth would move, but words would not come out; "it was as if you could not say them, even though you wanted to" (see 9.2). Her instinct about my capacity in this area is confirmed by researchers exploring motor differences in the autistic brain and their application to language.[248-249]

In the main, research stops at the point where it identifies the difference, and then presumes it to be a deficit. Sinclair,[214] an autistic commentator, talks about the transformational effect of being overtly taught what emotion words meant and how to use them in his life. Lartseva et al. [248] (p. 1) observe that "younger children with ASD have difficulties in acquiring and developing emotional concepts, and avoid using these in discourse". Difficulties in acquiring a skill via a particular route do not equate to that skill being out of reach. Like Sinclair, I did not learn automatically to use emotion words, but not learning in the same way as a neurotypical might did not mean I was unable to learn.

32

Extract from Sinclair:[214] 'Bridging the gaps: an inside-out view of autism'

Occasionally, under extreme circumstances such as the time I broke a bone, I was able to attach words to a subjective experience and make a simple statement such as "my foot hurts." Even when I could find words, no one believed me. I was told that I was only pretending to feel pain, fear, confusion, or whatever I was reporting because I really felt whatever the therapist's preferred theory predicted I should feel.

And through all this condescending concern about feelings and emotional issues, no one ever bothered to explain to me what the words meant! No one ever told me that they expected to see feelings on my face, or that it confused them when I used words without showing corresponding expressions. No one explained what the signals were or how to use them. They simply assumed that if they could not see my feelings, I could not feel them. I think this shows a serious lack of perspective-taking!

I finally started learning to talk about feelings when I was twenty-five. I knew someone then who taught me a vocabulary. She didn't know that was what she was doing. She didn't do it because she wanted to help an autistic person learn to "deal with" feelings. She just happened to be someone who talked a lot about her own feelings. She identified what each feeling was called, and where she felt it, and how it felt, and what her face and body were doing about it. When I asked questions about what the words meant, she explained. When she asked questions about my feelings, and I asked for clearer definitions of what she was asking, she clarified the questions until I could answer them. That's all it took to get started.

33

The beauty and dark side of stimming

Adapted from blog post[267] by Jessica Dark, neurodiversity specialist, mentor and blogger

TW

I am writing this sitting on my bed. Every time I pause to reread what I have written, my body pushes down onto the springs to create a rhythmic rocking motion. I read and bounce, rock and sway, my body does not like to stay still.

I am constantly in connection with the world around me. The world is so incredibly bright and extremely noisy but the same sensations that cause me pain and overload me also bring me so much joy and happiness. The bounce of my body and the swaying movements I make are sometimes referred to as stimming. This simply put just means that I like to receive the same sensation over and over as a form of comfort.

There is much controversy over the word 'stimming' as behaviourists like to correct these behaviours and see them as something 'abnormal', but there is nothing bad about my bouncing, swaying and continuous movement; it is in fact my happy place. As I move my body, I engage with the world in a way that I do not see from those without sensory sensitivities do.

I can be mesmer[i]sed by the sensory stimulation available in my environment, transfixed by the breeze swaying tree branches or ripples on the surface of the water in rivers and streams. I can smell the ground and the damp and the fresh crisp air. I can hear every moment in sound. I can see colours vibrant and clear.

I absorb my environment as part of my emotional processing. I feel love and comfort from just sitting next to the sea and watching waves crashing to the shore. I feel empowered by the beauty within art and music. I move my body because it helps me to think, it helps me to feel calm and relaxed. Stimming is my pleasure, it is my safe space, it is my calm.

Despite this, stims are not always beautiful. There is a dark side to stimming. When I was a teenager and processing the emotions after my father passed away, I would repeatedly hit my arm with a ruler. The pain cascading throughout my body brought balance within me, helping me process my internal pain through physical pain.

Some people create painful stims through repeatedly scratching their skin or repetitive chewing of finger nails until they bleed. Whilst not all stimming holds beauty, all stimming does hold purpose. Instead of taking away the need to physically process our world we can replace those angry, anxious stims with the ones that bring us joy. In doing this we can indeed turn our pain back into something beautiful again.

18.2 Emotional shutdown

Autistic brains have been shown to process emotions differently to neurotypical brains (see pop out box 31: 'Autistic emotional processing and research bias'). One of the most pronounced differences reported by autistics about their emotional landscape is the propensity of the emotional processing centres of their brain to shutdown. A neurotypical person might experience emotional shutdown once or twice in a lifetime in response to extreme circumstances: a horrific accident, the sudden death of a loved one. If you listen to people who have lived through such experiences, you might expect to hear them say something along the lines of "I felt numb" or even "I felt nothing". The experience was too big for their emotional capacity, it had a kind of white-out effect on their feelings. Whatever the feeling was that was required in response to the experience, it was too big and their brain, their heart, their emotions drew a blank. They felt nothingness.

Autistics report more frequent shutdown of emotional processing. Although they do shutdown in response to trauma as neurotypical brains do, in the main, autistic shutdowns do not appear connected to particular distress or upset. It is more as if there is a certain quantity of emotions (good or bad) each brain can process, and once it has reached its limit it shuts down. It is as though it performs an emotional reboot. For myself, I would expect to shutdown two or three times a month, more if a lot was going on (good or bad) and less if not so much was happening.

In shutdown I feel nothing. Prior to my getting diagnosed and reading about this aspect of brain function, shutdown had a huge effect on my life. It is a good example of where misdiagnosis can be dangerous, and where not seeming 'very autistic' can lead to that danger.

My tendency to shutdown has on several occasions been diagnosed by doctors as depression, and you can see why. I show up saying I do not feel anything, I look expressionless, downcast. I appear to be profoundly depressed. Diagnose me with depression and offer me medication and treatments for depression and you will be off on a well-intentioned good path. If, in that consultation, the doctor wondered, "is she autistic, could this be a shutdown?" then you are onto an altogether different and, to me, more fruitful path. (This distinction between the paths taken with and without an understanding of the autistic emotional landscape feeds into the mental health difficulties and health inequalities discussed in pop out boxes 17: 'Autism and mental health' and 24: 'Health inequalities and more'.)

18.3 Divorce

My first marriage (mentioned in sections 10.3 and 14.6) is a clear example of how great a difference understanding the distinction between normal autistic emotional processing and neurotypical mental illness can make. I married my husband in my mid-twenties and we began life as newlyweds. We had a tiny two-room house.

34

Experience of shutdown/meltdown

Anonymous

The author of this piece wished to remain anonymous. Unnamed it is easy to read these words as those of an emotionally unstable person who struggles with life and fails to connect with people. I know the author of these words and to think of them as in anyway incapable would be quite inaccurate. This person is a passionate successful school leader, who influences and accredits practice nationally and internationally, working in conjunction with many prominent organisations in the world of autism and learning disabilities.

(The author of this box deals with topics that overlap with content in section 18.5, and box 27: 'Suicide risk factors'.)

My mood has always either fluctuated from one extreme to another or been so flat as to feel unfeeling. I finally convinced the doctors to support me by granting me a hysterectomy just before my 30th birthday as I could no longer cope with the mood swings we put down to oestrogen. I will always say that this is the best move I ever made as it has meant I no longer feel like I am going mad each month. But, once the HRT levelled me out, I realised there had also been something else going on... I can reflect now and see there were long periods where I would experience shutdown (meltdowns too but these were/are explosive and last hours rather than days/weeks). The GP prescribed antidepressants and told me to take up a hobby. After many years of being unable to articulate what this feeling was, I had an intense need to leave. Suicide ideation plagued my thoughts. I left my home saying I was going to the shops, forwarded the calls from my mobile to my home phone and checked into a hotel where I 'hid' for 3 days.

Wracked with guilt for leaving the children and my husband, I slowly worked out how I could force myself to go back home. I didn't know what I was feeling, I was emotionless, flat, could not motivate myself to talk, or to ask for help. I find it hard to express how I feel because I find it difficult to discern between seemingly similar feelings.

I have been researching interoception for years to teach myself the differences. But there are many times when I just go on autopilot. Depressive meltdowns, shutdown, inertia, and an absolute wish for it all to stop. It's all consuming. Days spent in bed. Weeks without washing.

Executive function is the first thing to go. I don't remember how to look after myself. Eating, washing, talking, living. When I hit times of stress, I mask mask mask ... 'slap on the smile' and get on with life in public for as long as I can. Then – meltdown or shutdown. Meltdown rarely happens publicly because I fight them so hard, I know they are socially unacceptable, so they are internalised, but it has to go somewhere. Catatonia or shutdown creeps up on me.

One day I feel able to take on the world and then perseveration starts, thoughts become singular. Repetitive. Nothing new can enter my brain. So, the output slows, the input becomes restricted and I withdraw. It's like my brain has one thought and it's on loop. It's like the 'bokeh' effect. I am crisp and in focus, but everything around me becomes blurred and makes little sense. I have to wait my brain out, for it to refocus and the world becomes clear again.

I am still (in my mid-50s) explosive and prone to meltdowns at home. I mask for England when outside. I have few friends (but the ones I do have are very precious to me). I wonder at the adeptness of my peers in their abilities to understand each other. I spend an awful lot of time on my own and I like it like that. I find peopling difficult, draining and often withdraw. But I watch and I learn, I mimic my peers and hope they don't notice. I cope with situations that I fear may hurt without emotion. They are logged and filed and left to fester within. I marvel at my peers when they can recall events. I have forgotten more than I can remember about my youth as so much of it was spent in a state of shutdown (but I have only just realised that is why).

35

Experience of shutdown

Tigger Pritchard, autism and pathological demand avoidance advocate, consultant and trainer at www. tiggertraining.com

A dark viscous film begins to creep across my brain. As it encompasses my mind, my higher functions begin to dim. It feels like someone else is in charge, I cannot control it. I don't want to talk, don't want to hear, don't want to interact in any way. Lethargic, unsteady and lost.

It's not I don't want to:

I can't.

I need to vastly reduce all input NOW! This is survival. I have to reach my place of safety. I feel as if I'm in a slow-motion movie, slowly shutting down. Time perceived by me begins to move slower and slower. My usual sensory issues increase incredibly. Everything is TOO much.

My battery is almost completely discharged, I am on 5% and everything in me is on power save mode. Automatically I'm reacting to protect myself.

Survival sets in. I am exhausted, drained, limp, passive, inert. Everything I am slows down. I need to be alone, I collapse into my safe place, to recharge and survive. I am protecting ME, in failsafe mode. Often, it's my bed, I curl up, wrap the quilt around me and gently rock, reducing as much input as possible.

That's my shutdown: it has all been too much, the masking, my particular sensory and emotional overloads, they are all completely out of my control.

The time it takes me to recover varies, but I do recover.

The frequency of shutdowns differs from person to person, but I feel most individuals upon reflection can see a pattern of types, stretching back over many years.

This is not a meltdown. A meltdown is more visible, a shutdown is so much more personal and intimate and so much more serious long term. I'm learning to be more aware of me, of my needs, I have to be, and to discuss those needs with those very close to me.

The autistic brain has to exist in a neurotypical world, a world with neurotypical environments, neurotypical expectations of communication and sensation, neurotypical cultural ideals and so on. All of these things place stress on the autistic brain.

Am I aware of a 'shutdown' approaching? I did not used to be, but the more insight I have about myself, the more I realise I can take only so many events in succession before I need to opt for some self-care, some time to heal, or else shutdown will follow.

I have heard other people say, "I've had enough!" [or] "That's it, I'm off!" I think about that: no matter how that initial surge of brain chemicals and adrenalin may look to the outside world and feel to them, they were ultimately in some sort of 'self-control'. In that decisive moment, the moment when they recognised they needed everything to stop, in that moment they had the ability to 'count to ten', to 'deep breathe', to do something that enabled them to walk back into a complex situation after the initial surge of emotions had diminished. Their ability to counteract that overload is swift; often once out of the situation, they are able to be themselves once more. It is not the same with a shutdown. There is no control there, it is simply an act of survival.

36

Exploring student shutdown

Dawn Brown, assistant special school head teacher

I remember when I was training to be a teacher, back in the late 1990s, that SEN [Special Educational Needs] and accommodations or reasonable adjustments were a pipe dream away. Everyone was the same in all schools, following the National Curriculum and that was the same expectation in special education.

We beat around the bush and classed it a modified curriculum and taught discrete subjects in block[s] of one hour across every day. There was a break at 10.30, lunch at 12 and playtime that lasted for three-quarters of an hour. Teaching time was rigid, and we were expected to teach the subject on the timetable (whether it motivated or engaged or not!) for the length of time the timetable set, and rarely did we allow for movement breaks or twiddle toys.

The mantra of "work/first" came from our PECS [Picture Exchange Communication System] training, visual supports from our TEACCH* training along with structure and work delivered as 'tasks' in boxes. Working for rewards, built in using Now/Next boards became popular. I spent many hours coaxing learners from under tables (to join them under the table would not have been seen to be good practice) so they could re-join the group sitting on a chair at the table. This was the way children learned wasn't it?

I remember questioning why they sat beneath the tables. Old-school teachers would tell me it was non-compliance, "they know what they are doing", and that they were playing up. I questioned why sometimes some learners would enter the room and immediately seek a spot by the door to sit and sit and sit. Why some would stand at the threshold to the classroom not entering ... and I was always told it was because they were task avoidant.

I decided it was my job to come at this from a different angle, to find out what motivated and inspired the learners to come in, sit, and stay at the table, and I introduced quiet areas, sensory and practical learning stations, but this didn't always work. Why was this?

The more I watched, waited and reflected, the more I began to see that sometimes, the learners were unable to enter rather than unwilling. That they were struggling to make the transition into the room. That they retreated under the table rather than made the conscious decision to 'defy' staff by leaving the seat at the table. I began to ask what was going on, why is this happening, and why at the times it did?

I opened my eyes. I looked hard at my environment and I walked through doors at child's eye height. The world is very different from different angles – try it yourself... I had my team look at the room, what they were offering, the language they used, how often they spoke and even how many were speaking at once.

Once we had audited our behaviour, we could adapt it and see the impact [of] making what were sometimes small (to us) changes. We moved the visual clutter of the stripy mat that the children had to cross at the threshold of the room, and quickly realised that the sitting in the doorway was one learner's physical reaction to visual stimulus being overwhelming. He found it so difficult to cross that threshold, he would literally shutdown once he was in the room, and it would take him half an hour to recover.

Table-top activities in a class of seven SLD (severe learning disabilities) learners would never stay in the middle of the table, and would end up causing not only more visual stimulus, but also confusion about where to start/what piece to do next/whether mine is finished? This could lead to emotional overwhelm[edness], where the learners became so anxious, they would literally flee the situation and hide (under the table in some cases).

It wasn't common back then to recognise that bursts of work followed by bursts of physical activity/time to decompress was a great way to support learners who struggled in the classroom. It wasn't common to recognise that environments could affect the emotions of our learners, and it certainly wasn't common to allow learners the opportunity to have an escape route if this all became too difficult and led to shutdown.

When one learner's fight or flight kicked in, it was instantly recognisable as an explosion, whereas others were not so obvious as they merely withdrew and were 'no trouble'. We recognise this now as the freeze response, but to shutdown, to retreat from the environment because it is too much to cope with is as difficult to watch as the explosive responses when you know the why.

Autistic speakers such as Jamie and Lion[268-269] are very clear in detailing how the environment impacts on a person's ability to function, Intensive Interaction teaches us to watch and wait, and really listen to the actions of those we support, Studio 3 teaches the importance of empowering people to know their escape route and how to use it. For many, this may seem like common sense; but to many [others], this continues to baffle them. Until we support people (of every age) to recognise that there are safe ways out of the feelings of overwhelm[edness], confusion and anxiety, we will continue to watch them withdraw, shutdown, melt-down and hurt themselves and others. When I think back to all the times I was told, "they know how to push my buttons", I wonder how many times we knew how to push theirs.

* TEACCH = Teaching – Expanding – Appreciating – Collaborating and Cooperating – Holistic

I made us a dining room table for our lounge out of corrugated cardboard and covered it in photographs and magazine clippings. We sat on the floor, we did not own chairs, and hosted dinner parties for friends. We supported each other to get jobs we found fulfilling. We learnt to cook new foods, the novelty of cooking for someone else motivating our culinary forays. We even signed up to a veg box scheme. We were happy.

I was caught up in him and caught up in the story of us, and yet every so often, I would be sitting next to him on the sofa and would feel nothing. I would look across at this man, this beautiful kind man I supposedly loved, this man who proposed to me by flying me in a helicopter to a beach we had seen in a painting and offering me a ring he had designed himself, engraved with words deeply personal to me, this good man ... I would look at him and feel nothing.

I would notice the absence of an emotional response to him and think, "Goodness, what must this mean?" I knew there must be something terrible and dark at the heart of our relationship, how else would it be possible for me to look at him and not feel anything? I spent hours trying to work out what it was, was it a difference in interests, in intellectual capabilities, in earnings, in … in what? I could not put my finger on it.

And then the feelings would come back and I would look at him and feel besotted once again. I would file all the worrisome thoughts away and get on with the project of being young and in love and making house. We moved house. We agreed we would foster children instead of having our own.

Six weeks before we were due to get our first foster child, social services told us the house we lived in was not big enough. We managed to sell the house we had recently bought and buy another big enough one in that time. We began to foster; at first, we just had one little girl one day and one night a week. She had bright clear darting eyes, as big as grapes, and an infectious sense of mischief. She was autistic and an elective mute, which makes her sound uncommunicative – a notion that meeting her would quickly dispel. I was swept up in her wild beauty and impish nature. The plan going forward was to convert the loft into a double bedroom and foster with a view to adopting siblings as we knew that it was harder for them to find homes.

Each year as our wedding anniversary approached, I would alter slightly the wedding dress I had made to get married in, changing the neckline one year, removing a drapey bit another year, and then on the day of our anniversary, I would don it again and he would take a photo of me. The idea was that we would be able to watch through the years as bride and dress changed and aged, until somewhere in my sixties I would be wearing it as a scarf, but we would still be in love. Beauty is in the eye of the beholder and seen through his eyes I was beautiful whatever I wore, whether I was a young bride in a homemade dress or an older lady in a bedraggled scarf.

But.

But it kept happening, I kept finding myself in moments where I looked at him and felt nothing. Sometimes it would go on for days. There *was* something wrong, and although I did not know what it was, I knew it was there.

Somewhere around our fourth wedding anniversary we went out to dinner. And in a brutally kind conversation that neither of us can remember, we agreed we would get divorced. In our marriage ceremony we made 14 promises to each other, 12 of which we have kept to this day. Nothing can be a better test of "all that I have I share with you" than tearfully deciding together who will take the washing machine. I moved into a van whilst our house sold. Our foster child was found a different placement. Together we shopped for a flat for him, the estate agent mistaking us for the newlyweds we had been just a few years before.

Ten years after our divorce, I was diagnosed as autistic, and I read that emotional shutdown is part of the landscape of the autistic brain. Emotional shutdown was just one of the neuro differences that affected how we related to each other. Without either of us being aware of the differences, or understanding them, they contributed to the loss of that happily married life. In the weeks after my diagnosis, Radio 4's *The Listening Project* recorded an omnibus edition of my first husband and me reflecting on these differences.[270]

Last year I married again. There are days when I sit alongside my husband on the sofa and look at him and feel nothing. And on those days, I shrug and think, "I'll give it until the end of the week and see how I feel then". Invariably by the end of the week, my emotions have returned. I try to use the emotionless times to do activities that would under ordinary circumstances stir unpleasant emotions. No better time to do a boring task than when you cannot feel bored.

What was once absolutely devastating in my life has been reduced to little more than a shrug.

18.4 Dangers of misinterpretation

The misinterpretation of natural autistic emotional shutdown as abnormal neurotypical mental illness has had an effect on my mental health as well as on my relationships.

Before my first marriage, when I was on my own, I would experience shutdown. Having been told by doctors in the past that I was depressed, I always registered the sensation of shutdown as depression descending on me again. I would stare into the nothingness of those emotionless times and wonder what the point was.

It is very hard to find a point to life when you feel nothing, when you can look at the ones you love and feel nothing, when you move to do the things you are passionate about and feel nothing. If what you do in life, and those you love in life, do not excite emotion in you then what is the point of life? Misinterpreting shutdown as having meaning is in itself a suicide risk.

Post-diagnosis, it is the equivalent of my brain showing that little buffering display that comes up on computers as they struggle to load a vast file.

It sounds oxymoronic to say that emotional shutdown has a feel to it. But in the lack of emotion there is a sensation of sorts. I look at the world as if through a great many panes of glass, I can feel that my eyes stare more. On a day not spent in shutdown, my eyes would move around a room, focus and dance. But in shutdown they do not seem to move at all, they just fix in a default forward position and I turn my head to scan. I feel very far away from everything. Because embodied emotion is our presentness in our bodies, without that presentness you feel insubstantial. Poor interoception can make the world seem unreal to me; shutdown makes me feel unreal in the world, like a half thing, a spirit or a ghost, something ethereal, drifting about the place.

Often my voice loses its tone, my words come out in a monotone, and too slowly. This does not tend to be something I notice myself. I will begin a sentence and not realise I haven't finished it. This is something my son observes in his book, *My Mummy is Autistic*[271] – seen through his four-year-old eyes, my stopping in the middle of sentences is very obvious. It is also no big deal to him, he simply says, "so I remind her to keep talking". That works: I do have the other end of the sentence in my head, I will just have lost track of where I am in it and think that the whole sentence has been uttered when only a few words have been spoken.

227

At times, no words come out at all and I just stare. Like that moment before action at playgroup (4.1), I do not think I am not talking, not doing, to my mind I am in the process of doing. It is just that time in my mind is not running in parallel to time in the real world.

People who experience a surge of adrenalin in response to a dangerous situation often report that it felt as if time slowed down. Time, of course, runs at the same speed, but their brain's processing sped up in comparison to it, meaning they were better able to ensure their survival. It is a sensible chemical response to threat. As your processing races, time slows.

In shutdown, my processing slows and time blurs. There is more static around, I notice particularly things that do not move. I notice chairs, I stare at walls, I look at the concrete path from the gate to the front door of my house. I watch shadows. Sometimes the static, the unmovingness of things seems overwhelming and to move in such an unmoving place feels brash and uncouth. I slow, I stop.

For me, times that have a lot of emotional content, like family get-togethers at Christmas, or birthday parties, are particularly likely to trigger a shutdown. These are in no way traumatic, they are wonderful colourful events populated by people I love and trust. I just cannot keep up in my processing of them. I have a photograph that I return to often from a Christmas a few years ago. My son is three years old, I am lying on the floor and he is lying with me. His small arms are flung around my neck and his face, bright and loving, looks into mine.

18.5 The picture of my son and me

I look at this photo often. I find it very challenging.

I had gone upstairs to brush my teeth. Before climbing the stairs, I had said to my then boyfriend, now husband, "I am just going to brush my teeth". My son is from a different relationship and at this time my husband and I were dating and he was down on a visit to see me, so the "I am going to brush my teeth" was code for "can you watch my son for a moment?"

I brushed my teeth and as I crossed the landing back to the stairs, I caught sight of the rug beside my bed. It is a big dark brown rug with long textured fronds. It looked like it would feel good to lie on.

In my head the plan was just to detour and see how it felt. Just for a moment. I lay down. My son, having climbed the stairs to come and find me, lay down with me. My husband, who was watching my son, followed and snapped the little scene on the floor. It happened in seconds.

Only it did not.

Later that evening, my husband asked, "Do you realise you were lying on the floor for the best part of an hour?"

He listed the games he had played with my son whilst they waited for Mummy to finish brushing her teeth before they finally climbed the stairs together to find me.

Once I had been found, my son lay there with me for another half an hour or so, happy to have my attention, chatting away to me and stroking my face.

I look at the photo often. In it I see an aspect of me that I do not see in life.

I do not think of myself as someone unmoving on the floor.

I am generally very busy. People ask me: "Where do you get the energy?" "How do you do it all?" "Do you not want to rest?" I am always on the go.

I am not static.

Yet there in that photo is the evidence.

And more so … the doctor … that first GP … with his words, "You are clearly an excellent mother", what would he say if he saw that photo?

What if my husband hadn't been there?

Is this a good mother?

Is this dangerous?

My son is happy in the photo, he is accepting of me for who I am and how I am, especially with regard to my communication, or lack of it (as you can read in his book[271]) even when I am a nothing on the floor. The challenge in that love is huge. What have I to offer a love so big?

Looking back at past shutdowns offers some reassurance; it is not that there is a pattern to them, but there is a place. The place is sofas and downtimes. I have never shutdown in a work context, or when doing, I have never shutdown when solely responsible for my child. If I were to draw a different analogy, I would draw one of a car engine thrashing itself to some point of no return, but that continues whilst it is being driven, getting hotter, revving more, but continuing and it is only once stopped that it does not restart.

I would say that, although the need to shutdown stems from an accumulation of social contact requiring processing, the shutdowns themselves are triggered by pauses; at moments in which relaxing is possible. This is probably why, for me, they happen during holiday times, at Christmas, or long birthday weekends, times that generally have less work to do in them and more people around to share responsibility with.

19 Pregnancy (explanations of a photoblog)

Throughout the reading of this book, you have known I am pregnant. This book has been more of a journey than I ever imagined it being as I set out to write it, I have discovered things about myself with you as the pages have turned. It seems only fair to give you all the information I have to hand even if I cannot quite be sure where it fits; with your outside perspective, you may be able to see something here that I cannot. This chapter contains photoblog posts I wrote about my experience of being autistic and pregnant. As with Chapter 16, the titles of these posts are descriptions of the photographs that accompanied them when I originally wrote them.

19.1 A pack of information about pregnancy

Pregnancy comes with an overload of information and a dramatic increase in my sense of smell, making the olfactory world overwhelming at times.

All my appointments, scans, midwives, vaccines, blood tests etc. have to be arranged on the phone. In most areas of life (aside from my private life), I would challenge anyone to know I was autistic. I have practised all my NT [neurotypical] moves and I do a pretty convincing impression if you are not looking for the tells [body language, verbal tics, etc.]. But the phone is something I have yet to master. Despite having run my own business for ten years, I still never give out a phone number. Pregnancy has been challenging.

This week we went for our first scan, after which we were fed through a veritable obstacle course of medical checks (even with opting not to have screening). Each one was a different person in a different room, I had only known I was going to one of these, so only prepared one social interaction in my head. The rest came as surprises. But I did as I was told and my husband has an easy charm and a ready laugh, he gets us through most social situations. It was all easy enough, fine, until the very last appointment of the assault course.

The final appointment was for my 'wellness'. We walked into the room. One woman was sat at a computer, with a chair adjacent to the desk facing outwards as often happens at doctor's surgeries. I can talk easily with that set up. The other person looks at their computer screen, I stare off into the distance, we are all happy. But this was different: a second woman sat on a chair directly opposite the chair I presumed was mine. Straight on opposite, almost close enough for our knees to touch.

I was so shocked by the set up that I glanced back at my husband, who was by this point half shrouded in all the things we had been given that he had to carry and was arranging himself on a more distant chair near the door.

Everyone in the room was looking at me. The ladies began to greet me. I looked at the chair trying to work out how to sit on it, and back at my husband who smiled understandingly and gave a sort of "what can we do shrug" together with a "you'll be alright smile". Encouraged, I sat down.

I had not replied to any of the greetings, so the ladies were beginning to look puzzled. The one at the computer busied herself, the other re-emphasised her gaze directly at me, as you would a child whose attention you were trying to get.

I physically lifted myself up on my chair with one hand pressed into the seat and tried to find a different way to sit. I was panicking. I knew I had done the situation wrong this far. I was frantically trying to find a way to sit that would make me normal.

But it was too late.

"Are you okay?" the cheerful lady asked.

She was so chipper I actually felt a bit angry with her. Indignant. Who sets chairs up facing directly at each other without even a table in between? Surely even in the NT world that is not an okay way to set up a room.

"Sorry," I sputtered, "I just find the set up a bit confrontational".

She smiled at me like anything I said was perfectly fine and she was willing to listen to my silliness and placate it, then tell me the important things about not smoking, drinking, eating my greens etc.

It had not worked. So I tried again.

"It is just that I am autistic," I said, "I find face to face like this difficult".

"That is okay," she said and ploughed straight on with asking me questions and testing my carbon monoxide levels whilst I physically squirmed in the chair.

My husband remarked afterwards, "she said 'that is okay', and then did nothing about it."

What she meant is, "I do not mind if you behave weirdly in front of me, I will just act like you are normal. Because normal is desirable. So I will pretend you are normal as a compliment to you."

Not, "I recognise you are different and will make the adjustments I can to help you not be uncomfortable."

In this particular situation, that would have been her turning her chair slightly. I could not turn mine because it was up against the desk.

I was fine. I passed all the questions. Turns out I do not smoke, I eat my veg, I stopped drinking the minute I knew I was pregnant, I have not been exposed to carbon monoxide and do about five exercise classes a week (phrased as "Are you managing to keep active?").

But someone else would struggle more than me, in this situation or another. And just being okay with us looking weird is not kind. Neither is pretending everyone is the same. Often adjustments are very simple. Turning a chair, switching off a light. I do not think these things should be

234

done because someone has a particular condition or other, they should be done simply as acts of kindness [from] one human to another.

19.2 A urine sample pot

Yesterday on my way to my midwife appointment, I spilt my urine sample, not once, but twice!

I also spent the journey reciting aloud the sentences I had thought might be needed for our conversations. I practised them out loud in the car on my own, so that they would sound natural, friendly, casual – not practised.

I have been writing these sentences in the background of my mind for about a week.

I knew I would have a blood test, so I figured there would be something to say about needles, I knew I would be asked about [the] baby kicking, I knew I would have to hand over the wee.

But mostly I did not know what would be said, which meant a more expansive list of sentences needed to be practised.

This is not unusual. For me it's standard practice in any circumstance. I only realised other people do not do this recently when I read a post from someone online who had just realised the same. They said, "I thought everyone did this!" And I read that and thought, "They do." But from reading the comments, I learned they do not.

When I worked in a special school, I supported many autistic students. One young man springs to mind. He was about seven years old and had a set of good sentences, between which he would choose in any given circumstance. Admittedly lots had been learned from *Thomas the Tank Engine*, so did not always have immediate application to life, but he did a grand job using what he had.

His speech, his diction, his enunciation of all the words was perfect. But he only had those phrases.

I remember a particularly chaotic class outing, when we had finally got everyone to the classroom door, coats on, medical kits in bags, inhalers remembered and so on. I got ready to do the obligatory head count and as I scanned the room, I realised that by some miracle, this young man had remained untouched by the pandemonium of preparing to leave the room.

He was sat in a puddle of sunlight on the carpet contentedly playing with some bricks.

I shouted his name! He startled and looked up, instantly understanding where he was supposed to be. He needed to answer my shout. I saw his head scan through the sentences available to him:

"But wait!" he cried in reply, "We've left the refreshment lady behind!"

It was a brilliant response, the timing perfect, all of the tension of "Are we ready yet, has so and so got their coat on, is the risk assessment done?" was instantly dissolved.

Across the spectrum, planning what you say, preparing for conversations, is a 'thing'.

His example shows how someone could struggle to communicate without enough phrases to hand. I can make up as many phrases as I like, but I cannot always predict what I will need.

My story is also an example of how being autistic can change the health care you receive. My autism is hidden to those caring for me (unless they take note of wherever it is in my file that says 'autistic').

I had three questions I wanted to ask. Three additional utterances outside of the conversation I had imagined. None of these questions were urgent: do not be concerned. But I did not get to ask any of them.

I had to use all of my communication skills to keep pace with the natural flow of conversation. I got to use a good number of my prepared sentences but also had to quickly construct sentences in real time. The effort of doing that meant I had no effort left over to work out where in our spontaneous conversations my questions could be asked.

236

My diagnosis of autistic still means something even though I can hide it if I choose to.

Someone who noticed that diagnosis in my notes might take into account the increased effort it might be taking me to conduct a 'normal' conversation, and might offer opportunities for me to ask questions. In a daydream world they would tell me before I got there what I would be asked when I was there.

And in a daydream world I would not spill my wee!

19.3 A scrap of paper with a few inadequate notes scrawled upon it

My plan, in any given situation, is often not to be autistic.

It is often other people's plan for me too.

I dress it up for myself in a variety of ways: next time I will know what to wear, next time I will not be so nervous, next time I will understand what is expected better, next time I will not make the same mistakes. But it amounts to the same thing: next time I will not be autistic.

Well, I did do better at my midwife appointment this time: this time I did not spill my wee!

But that is about as far as the achievements go.

I am the last woman my midwife sees in her surgery. She is usually running about an hour late by the time she gets to my appointment (running to time is made all the harder for her as she works to clean the room between women as per the new COVID-19 guidance).

I wonder if she has an afternoon surgery somewhere else. I wonder if I am her lunch break. I imagine her morning, an endless sea of the same conversations, each one routine to her, but significant to the women she sees.

I imagine the questions the women will have asked her. Pregnancy heightens a woman's senses, and concern for an unborn child will make even the tiniest of changes in sensation flag themselves up as a warning sign. No doubt she has reassured everyone that their particular observations are "normal for pregnancy". She has probably heard each particular concern a million times over in her career before, but she treats every conversation as new, shows foolish worries a respect they do not deserve, and all the while listens out for the observation that may indeed be a red flag.

I like to think I am a good patient. I do not ask her anything. I imagine I am a relief as I do not trouble her with lists of things that are normal for pregnancy. I am easy to process, she just has to take my blood pressure, do the standard checks and I will be gone, and the next part of her day can begin.

At my last appointment (aside from spilling the wee sample, that I am obliged to bring, twice on my journey to her) I excelled.

I was fun, I made her laugh, I wore leggings with an underwater scene of otters swimming with rainbows the like of which she said she had never seen before. I offered her reassurance on the current crisis, and when she said it was a difficult time to be pregnant, I balanced this perspective with stories from lives that really are difficult during this time, not my privileged comfortable life.

But.

I came home, and I did not know what she had said. I knew there were to be scans because I am 'high risk'. But I did not know where or when. I knew I had been told other things, but I did not know what.

Together my husband and I went through the folder of notes she keeps, but the numbers in columns in tiny boxes did not give us the answers we were looking for. Inside the green cardboard front cover of my file were a list of numbers I knew she had written when talking to me ... were they about scans, or were they about appointments with her, or something else?

I did not know.

Last time I went with three questions to ask, and asked none of them. I was too busy being a lovely patient.

This time would be different.

Because this time I would take notes.

238

I took a notepad with me. Before the appointment I reminded myself not to perform my perfect patient role. "Concentrate Jo," I scolded.

I laid the notepad out as soon as I got into the room. I did not look up from the floor. I did not offer any small talk, nor pick up on her offer about how hot the weather is. I looked at the notepad. On it, before entering the room, I had written "scan?" I was going to listen for when my scans were to be.

I did not ask.

I just waited, presuming it would come up.

She began the routine of checks. My blood pressure was taken. "Can I have your tummy?" I was lying on the bed. My tummy was right in front of me. She waited. I did not understand. "Can I?" she gestured. Damnit, I gave myself a mental kick, remembering from the visits before that she needs skin not frock. She had not asked me to undress. I lifted my dress. She manipulated my bump.

"You must be uncomfortable with the baby lying like that." I nodded.

She walked to her desk, and I got up.

"You missed your 32-week scan?" she said as she flicked through pages in the folder of information,

"You're due to have them at 32 weeks, __weeks and __ weeks."

I wrote, "32". I do not know what the other numbers she said were.

"You should have had a letter?"

"I didn't get a letter."

"Did they phone?"

"No."

"You're not the first person this has happened to, letters seem to be going missing, shall I get them to phone you next time?"

I looked at my notes, at the gaps in information. My plan to take notes was not making me any less autistic.

Autistic people process language slower than neurotypical people.

(Perhaps we take it in at greater depth, maybe it is quality over quantity? In this situation it is not useful, in another it might be.)

What good would it be if someone phoned me and gave me information that I could not take in, and could not note down adequately? I felt helpless.

"Your next one is at 36 weeks, I'll ring them and check they have that in."

I wrote down "36" and circled it. It was one of the numbers I had missed earlier.

So far, I had done nothing but listen intently and answer direct questions laconically. But I knew I had a piece of information that was relevant here. I was not keen on saying it.

"I did have 48 hours of contractions," I forced myself to confess. "I couldn't sleep, they wouldn't stop."

"Oh? When was that?" She said this in mild tones.

My guess would be the 'Oh' is the clue. If I had said I have been feeling too hot at night, or a lot of pressure on my bladder or whatever one of the other small and common concerns might be, then I do not think I would have got the 'Oh'. I think the tone would have been the same, it is the tone chosen to not alarm someone.

"Two or three weeks ago," I hedged, ashamed to say they were four days before our last appointment and that I had not mentioned them. Why spoil the performance of a lifetime when you are wearing otter leggings with rainbows on them?

"And did you ring?"

"No."

She looked a little stumped.

"I'm not very good with the phone," I offered. In my head adding: especially when I actually need help. In essence I have no way of contacting you in an emergency that I can access. "I'm not very good at asking for help."

I did not tell my husband until a day and a half in. And I only told him then because I thought it was strange that he did not look more concerned. Why wasn't he frightened? After all, this is my second child, but his first, shouldn't he be more worried than me (I am already well versed in how normal every weird thing about pregnancy is – your eyeballs swell up?! Normal … everything is flippin' normal!)

I watched him getting on with his project to turn our scrappy back yard into a raised-bed wonder. Maybe it is because I have not told him, I thought to myself. So I asked him why he wasn't worried, and he asked what there was to worry about. It turned out I had not told him.

"I didn't tell my husband," I offered as a joke, and she took it and laughed.

"Shall we see if I can get them to book you a 32-week scan now?"

I nodded, the information had done its job. She rang.

"There, that's done. Next time tell your husband and give us a ring. But you should be fine, and with that scan you get to see your baby tomorrow!"

(Translation: next time, do not be autistic).

I also have to re-book all my appointments with her because a system is changing … over the phone, it cannot be done in person when I am there with her, and the appointments I had already booked cannot be moved.

The other failure was a question about whooping cough vaccination – have I had it?

I do not know.

I remember going and waiting at a surgery, but I do not remember the appointment, what was said or what was done to me. Most likely that was the vaccination, I cannot think of what else it would have been.

I came home feeling humiliated. I had told my husband not to worry, that this time I would take notes (i.e. not be autistic) and yet this scrap of paper is all the understanding I b[r]ought home from an appointment that lasted over half an hour.

I am not incapable, my brain is very good. I would not want to change it. It has extraordinary capacity in some areas (balanced by the next to none in others). Having the duff bits of yourself on display is as disheartening as having the great bits of yourself cheered is heartening.

It would take very few adjustments to make this appointment accessible to me:

Write down the key information I need.

Ask me directly if I have any questions.

Give me a way of getting in touch that is not a phone number.

(Incidentally I have been given an email address, but I do not know where, I suspect it was by a kind soul on Facebook.)

My notes are very clear about me being autistic. But the woman my midwife meets appears like all the other women she meets and so gets treated the same.

If the word autistic, in this context, meant something, that could potentially make a difference to my health and to the health of my unborn child.

The adjustments suggested would not just help me, and other autistics. The last time I posted something of this ilk, people with anxiety commented that they struggle too, and I know people who struggle specifically with doctors and not elsewhere. I have a friend whose blood pressure always reads as high at the doctor's, to such an extent that they now ask her to take her own readings at home.

I am not anxious. My blood pressure reads well within normal. I just process information differently.

19.4 Me with a newborn standing in a beam of sunlight in an orchard outside a small cottage hospital in Germany

I had my first child in Germany.

He was born in a cottage hospital that was more like a spa than anything we would recognise as a hospital in the UK. Each room had its own balcony with lavender planted outside, it was set in an orchard. In the morning, people asked you what you would like to eat and through the day you would be served the meals of your choice, as well as being b[r]ought fruit juices and 'breastfeeding tea'.

The picture is me and my son when he was a few days old. The whole experience was as idyllic as it looks.

As my last few posts on this topic testify, this time around it has not been seeming so idyllic, and the rapidly approaching prospect of giving birth during a pandemic has loomed large on the horizon.

When I lived in Germany, I often speculated that the culture made being autistic easier. People said what they meant, people were direct, and that I was direct back did not stand out, it was normal.

I did not experience any communication difficulties during my first pregnancy. Whereas this pregnancy has been a stern lesson in my own limitations, one that at times has been quite humiliating.

But today things changed.

It is true that the experience of difference changes against different backdrops, and that aspects of cultural differences have an effect. But I do not think being in Germany made me magically not autistic. It just hid a few things from view.

I never had a problem exchanging information during appointments, because no one ever expected me to do it. I never had a problem getting the information because no one expected me to understand it. Because there was no expectation of language processing, everything was written down for me, and any questions that needed answering were very carefully and clearly set out for me.

In labour, I did not have to contend with direct instructions, or try to engage in chit chat, because I had no common language with my midwife (I did speak some German, I was better at reading and listening to German, but the midwife who supported me was not German and spoke no English). All support was given practically or through simply being a silent calming presence.

This time around, I have been confronted with all that you have read about and more that I have not shared. But today...

Today my husband attended the appointment with me. This is not allowed in lockdown, but can be allowed for those who need it as a 'reasonable adjustment' (those are the magic words).

This happened because the autistic community told me I should ask for it. And I told my husband I would not, and that I did not like being told what to do. I am perfectly capable and can manage myself... Only I had no evidence of that capability or tha[t] managing, as I have not been able to bring home from the appointments a working knowledge of what has been said. He phoned and spoke to someone on my behalf.

Following the advice of the autistic community (whilst simultaneously complaining about doing so – Grace by name but not by nature!), I moved the information about my autism from somewhere within the folder of notes to a sticker on the front of it.

And copying an example set by a fierce neurodivergent friend, I wrote a one- page clear explanation of what my diagnosis means in this context:

- That although I respond to conversation as it is happening, I do not process the meaning until later, which means [that] in appointments I cannot ask follow-up questions in response to what has been said, and I cannot use the phone effectively.

- That I find eye contact confrontational not comforting (Thank you to friends on here [this blog] for telling me that midwives are taught to actively give eye contact in order to reassure people who seem distressed – it was very alarming to think that if I was distressed, the eye contact levels might have gone up).

- That my registry of internal sensations is atypical, meaning I may report things like pain or temperature idiosyncratically.

I worried in the car on the way to the appointment that my husband would not be allowed in, and that we might be in a waiting room with other people and need to explain why he was there. I coached him on what he should say (I only allowed one short sentence) and instructed him that if the conversation went any other way, he was to concede and allow me to go to the appointment on my own. I did not want us to mess up a social situation.

(There is no way he would have followed these instructions had that situation arisen ... he does not follow orders well, but I tried.)

When we got there, we were BOTH welcomed in immediately. The midwife and her manager commented on how useful the note on the front of the file was, and when they found the one-page summary, they asked if they could take a copy and share it ahead with the team likely to support me at the birth.

For the rest of the appointment, things were noted down for me. It was agreed [that] my husband's phone, and not mine, would be the main point of contact. And so on... Everything suddenly became effortless and as a consequence, I heard that my baby has finally turned around, I heard his heartbeat, I came away knowing when I get to go back next.

I am home now and it feels like I have been given back the joy of late pregnancy. It had become a set of worries that I was denying I had. And now it is just a lovely thing again, to be grateful for.

With those adjustments in place, I can go to the appointments on my own, and can come home feeling like I have done them well. They have taken away all the looming nastiness and replaced it with a future that looks as lovely as the experience I had first time around.

I have written to thank them. The adjustments they made will feel small to them, they write a note, they text instead of phoning, but they are huge to me and go beyond just worrying about pregnancy to affecting how I think of myself.

It is a very sobering thought to think of the contrast between my experience, which is one of very little need, and the experience of people who lead far more challenged lives.

I am nearly 34 weeks pregnant. It has taken me, as a capable individual, able to articulate and write down my needs, 34 weeks to ask for some relatively minor adjustments which make the world of difference to me.

What if I were less able to self-advocate?

What if the adjustments I needed were more significant?

20 Special interests

Autistics are renowned for having what are commonly referred to as 'special interests'. A special interest is a topic to which an autistic person devotes their exceptional capacity for focus and on which they lavish their cognitive skills. Having a special interest is one of the most common characteristics of autism and yet until I wrote this book, I would not have been certain I had one. In this chapter, I realise what my special interest is in life.

37

Female autistics, late diagnosis, masking and relationships

Autistic women tend to get diagnosed later than autistic men, misdiagnosed or not diagnosed at all.[80,272–275]

One of the barriers to diagnosis for women is the perpetuation of the idea that autism is a male condition. It is only recently that the gender difference in diagnosis has been questioned and people are considering whether the old rule of thumb of there being one autistic girl to every four autistic boys is true, or whether it is a product of gender bias in the diagnostic process.[71,75–79]

A further barrier to diagnosis for women is a lack of understanding of the different ways in which autism presents in males and females.[81–82,272,276] The female

presentation of autism has largely been ignored in research.[73-74] If people are using tools designed to identify male autistics, and female autistics present differently, then it is not surprising that these tools do not identify female autistics.

It is interesting to note that where autism occurs alongside severe cognitive impairments, the gender ratio is closer to 1:1, whereas in those with average to high intellectual function, it is closer to eight boys to one girl. This could suggest that only the easy to spot females are being identified.[56]

Professor Barry Carpenter (p. 8) warns "We have an undiagnosed population here, who are currently not getting the best from our education system".[71] A late diagnosis, misdiagnosis, or no diagnosis at all is not only a risk to a woman's education, it can have an impact on women's wellbeing[71,273] and their ability to achieve their full potential academically,[277] professionally[56,72] and in their personal lives. Researchers[278] note the consequences in the long-term of failing to diagnose women can be severe.

NASEN's[71] report on autistic girls flying under the radar notes (p. 3) that despite having social communication difficulties similar to, or at higher levels than males, "intellectually able girls and women with ASC have better social integration skills" than male autistics. Autistic women are more likely to channel their efforts into perfecting masking[71,272,276,279-284] than autistic men.

Someone masking makes every effort to try to understand the social world around them and fit into it as best they can. NASEN[71] notes that autistic girls may rote-learn conversational phrases or copy social behaviours they witness around themselves or on television. In their efforts to be successful in relationships, they may focus on a single relationship in an intense manner which can be difficult for both parties.[86] And yet in spite of all their work, "in every social situation, instead of socialising with little effort, they struggle to conform and to generate acceptable responses and behaviours" (p. 3).[71]

Masking can be a threat to self-perception[285] with many autistics spending so much time and concentration on perfecting their mask that they lose sight of who they truly are beneath it. The effort of masking can lead to social exhaustion[186,274,285] and has long-term mental health consequences.[204–205,277,279,283,286–291]

20.1 My special interest

Many autistics have topics that particularly interest them, subjects that they enjoy focusing their brain's extraordinary capacity for acquiring knowledge upon. Had you asked me what my 'special interest' was prior to my writing this book, I would probably have answered that it was my work.

It is my work that I spend my time thinking about. It is in my work that I most use my brain's capacity for acquiring and processing information.

But my work does not hold the same obsessional grip over me that other people's interests hold over them.

Writing this book has shown me that there *is* one topic I have been interested in for nearly my whole life. An interest that began when I was seven years old and has not relented yet.

An interest I studied through my childhood and teenage years, an interest I pick up in every television programme I watch and every book I read. It is the topic I most want to talk about with friends and the topic my brain returns to as soon as I close the doors of work in my mind. Which is not to say it is not there in my work, it is very much a part of my work as well. It permeates the whole of my life.

My interest is in relationships. I have spent my whole life trying to figure them out, to work out how to have them and maintain them. Whether they are friendships, working relationships or intimate relationships. Rather than engaging in small talk, I want to talk about the machinations of people's private lives. This book is my half of that conversation, and I am hugely indebted to the people who have contributed their own insights from their private lives to the pop out boxes within the text.

I wonder how my relationships would change if I accepted myself as autistic, if I adopted an autistic identity? Would I stop trying to solve them with the solution to be more neurotypical and begin to look at them in other ways?

I need new stories, ones that have a like-me protagonist in them. I keep trying to write the story of how love works across the neuro divide, but it is evidently not a story I know.

Instead of me working out the story, kind friends have shared their stories with me for this book:

38

Doing important things that make no sense

Rachel Barker, lead practitioner in an area special needs school, MEd student in SPMLD, golf enthusiast and wakeboarder

Being in a relationship with some[one] who is not autistic is doing a lot of things that make no sense to you but seem to matter to them. The world often expects people who are neurodiverse to adapt to them but in relationships the other person is supposed to work with you. And that works both ways. So yes, being in a relationship with someone who isn't autistic finds you doing a lot of things that just simply seem bizarre. Interestingly enough, those subtle aspects of autism present in my day-to-day interactions have been as

much the [reason for the] attraction to me as the downfall of the relationship.

One ex described me as enigmatic. The same ex also found my difficulty to discuss my emotions problematic. The issue is that they are actually the same trait – I am not enigmatic, I'm just not very in touch with my emotions! This might be appealing at the start of a relationship, the chase, the honeymoon period, but in my experience hasn't led to very successful long-term relationships. I was, and still am, resistant to doing things not 'my way'. Relationships tend to require lots of compromise, lots of honesty (which also respects the other person's feelings) and lots of talking. All of these are complex for me. Relationships are essentially a minefield.

Currently, and unknown to both of us initially, I am in a relationship with someone else that is autistic. The diagnosis for both of us has allowed us to accept and view each other differently. It has opened up new channels of communications that work for both of us.

We still end up doing lots of things that make no sense to each other but we can talk about that now. In fact, we have reconfigured our communication to do just this. We have agreed topics for different methods of communication – WhatsApp and text messages have different purposes. I particularly struggle with talking when I am stressed and anxious so I have an app on my phone that read[s] text aloud. She prefers it when I am more structured in my communication and this also helps me to stay on topic.

We each have certain non-negotiables, but we have set up our house to manage both of our needs. We have a dinner chart on the wall – both of us find it hard to plan dinner after a long day at work and this takes the stress out of it. I loathe doing a food shop but can work with adding food we need to the board and doing it online. She prefers an electronic list, so then adds the board contributions there for the online shop. It is long-winded but means less stress for both of us. Each of us thinks our way is more efficient but this is a structure we can both use.

Occasionally, we surprise each other with the reasons we do things. She once asked me why I don't always put my shoes on the rack (it had clearly been bugging her). I said, sometimes my hands are full when I come in and you don't like me to walk through the house in shoes, so I take them off with the other foot and don't have the hands to pick them up. I thought I was doing the thing she liked (not walking through the house with shoes on); she thought I was deliberately doing something that annoyed her. Compromise is not always the most successful form of communication. (I usually pick my shoes up now in case you wondered.) Another thing I find really difficult is my stuff being moved, she hates clutter. We have agreed drawers now for certain items and she has learnt to accept that moving others is bound to end in an argument.

But it is not just the day-to-day things that become difficult in a relationship when you are autistic (although these are sometimes the things you might get most stuck on). The emotional stuff can also be really tough. I do not like talking about my emotions. I don't even know what my emotions are half the time. The app helps but sometimes I do just lose language temporarily. My other half has learned to recognise the signs [that] I am overwhelmed (usually before I do) and again, we have strategies that we know work for us – it has been a lot of trial and error and misunderstanding, but right now, we have some pretty good structures in place that work for us. And I have learnt to recognise that sometimes her face is just asleep and she really is fine!

39

Thirty-five years and counting

Anonymous

We met in the mid-1980s, I had spent so long masking with a massive grin on my face, he was withdrawn, shy and hid behind a group of outgoing friends. You couldn't have found two people more different. He fished and enjoyed his own company. I surrounded myself with people because I thought that's what people did. I felt like it wouldn't be accepted if I wasn't like everyone else. I craved security and that was supposedly in the form of love. If someone loved me, they would know me, and I would love them, and it would all fall into place.

Relationships are hard. They aren't like a Mills & Boon novel (well not always) and they aren't like in the movies (even *Die Hard*), and they aren't like in a young girl's dreams.

What they are like is hard.

But they do get better as we learn about each other, the things that when we give, they will take and those things they won't take. When we met, we were as neurodivergent as we are now, but we have learned a lot about each other. He helped me to see that I don't have to 'people' to be valid as a person. I can enjoy my own company and still be seen as a social being. He has supported me through the most tempestuous of times, and while the road has been incredibly bumpy, we remain here together 35 years on.

I have now been with him for twice as long as I was without him. Scary thought! We spend days apart living in the same house. Him working or studying (he has intense interest in being the best he can be at his job) in one room and me inert and watching TV in another. He goes out for bike rides that last three hours and I ... well I don't. I read fiction, he reads non-fiction, history and war ... but what we do together is have a deep understanding that although we may not be in the same physical space, we are there.

We share a very strange sense of humour, one that makes us laugh like drains at some of the most stupid stuff. We have a language we share, including a dialect that is shared by our children, and is local to just our house (like the way we pronounce coriander) and we remember that the world is actually a hilarious place to live if you look at it from the right angle. We support each other emotionally – recognising in the other person the emotions they might not recognise them-selves. Well, okay, not always.

We know to leave the other alone for a bit of decom-pression time when they arrive home from work. But we no longer have the 'ding dongs' and the hugely explosive fall outs that after many years we can reflect back on as two very different minds trying to find a middle ground. Some days we don't speak for hours, and we settle into a place of sharing space in the evenings without pressure to discuss, debate, or right the world's wrongs.

Don't get me wrong, there are times when that happens (especially if there is something reported about environmental issues as that is another intense interest of his!) with the two of us having very strong opinions that don't always match. But we are able now to agree to disagree or put the differences to one side (not always). There are, of course, certain things that we cannot compromise on ... his cycling and my need for routine are the most obvious, but there are now many more things that we do compromise on.

It took us time, long discussions and many 'ding dongs' to get here. We have raised two children, both grown and living with their partners, and that was something that took all our powers of compromise. While he is so laid back, he is almost horizontal in his approach to parenting, I have needed to have structure and routine. This has caused some falling out but seems to have been successful as our children are both amazing and successful people. So, while we continue to be very different people, neurodivergence doesn't mean that all things are impossible. It means that there was a lot of work involved in creating a space where I could be myself, just the myself that's in a relationship.

40

A neurodiverse marriage

Anonymous

We have been married for nearly 30 years. Neither of us knew we were neurodiverse when we started out. We've had to make it up and work it out as we went along. One strong aspect for us is our commitment. When we made those promises in church to stick by each other no matter what we went through, we meant it, and so at times, the only thing that stopped us splitting up, was the fact we didn't believe in splitting up!

Hubby now self-identifies as being autistic and I as ADHD. Knowing that has been illuminating. The biggest problem we've had is to learn each other's mode of communication. It was really hard with each of [us] expecting the other to know what we were thinking in the first 16 years or so. It was only as we learned about ourselves, and dared to give it a label that things started improving. We learned this during two lots of counselling. The counselling was brilliant for us as it taught us how to listen to one another. For example, I now understood that his anger at people chewing, tapping on keyboards or having the windows open in the summer, was because he has hyper sensitivity to certain sounds. He now knows that when I get up in the middle of a film or interrupt him mid-sentence, it's because my brain is on hyperactive mode and I NEED to move or blurt out what's in my head. We have learned to be forgiving and communicate better. (Or go and do something in a different room!)

We do things like make appointments to have a row … well, talk things out, which gives both of us the processing time to prepare how to explain what is upsetting us. We have a rule to listen and not verbally attack or blame the [other] person. We also have a very quiet, tidy and organised house (hubby) and seem to balance each other out most of the time. That doesn't mean we get on all the time! I have learned to get my social fix with friendships, to go to parties on my own and give him time to process. Every holiday is planned with a timetable, we have a weekly meal plan and all those things help hubby have predictability and me with my executive function difficulties. We try to laugh a lot, go out to things we both enjoy, like theatre, gigs and long walks and remember that we are only human.

41

Love across a neuro-divide

T & C

One neurotypical, one not, but both in love with each other.

Let me give some examples of early on in our relationship, funny as some may seem, they were major hurdles for us to overcome, causing both of us huge levels of anxiety.

(NT = neurotypical partner; ND = neurodivergent partner)

ND: That's the wrong side of the road to walk upon

NT: What! He's telling me what side of the road to walk on, what is he like!

ND: So, what time will we be leaving the party?

NT: Oh, it will be finished by 11pm easily.

11.10pm. He just sat there, totally disinterested, arms crossed and ready to go, ignoring everyone. I could not believe how rude he was!

ND: Marks & Spencer's black boxer shorts, cotton, with a blue line around the top rim. All was well. I needed these to be the same, I may have already had 12 or so pairs, but some were wearing out, so I needed some more.

But M&S changed the style ... me, utter panic, we went to every M&S in our county, I rang stores across the other counties and searched online, I was gutted, troubled and highly anxious, I spent ages looking for these exact matching items.

NT: He took ages, I could not believe just how many hours he spent looking for those pants. Are they really that important?

This was a turning point for her, as she came to understand that many weeks/months/years of my life had been spent looking for the 'right items'. She came to realise that this was something she would have to get used to, but at the same time felt sure there were ways make these 'right items' journeys less painful for her (and in some ways she has).

NT: Do you have any more songs you know; all you ever do is whistle those same songs all the time!

ND: ....

ND: ....

NT: You can't say that, it's so rude!

We could give so many more, but these examples show how differently our minds work. To me, the pants were of utmost importance, to me I was told the party would be over by 11pm, and the side of the road to walk upon, why that's the Highway Code! All utterly clear-cut and fully understandable to me. Those songs I whistle, safe, secure, and comforting, especially in times of stress. I do also have a habit of saying stuff that is a little too honest.

To her, an absolute minefield, the misunderstandings caused by the differences in how our minds work caused us lots of pain and anxiety and almost led to us breaking up. We are, however, several years later, thankfully still together. So how?

We have had to learn to listen, to be open, incredibly so, to compromise, and to develop our own strategies, for us, for our relationship. We have recently together started exploring insights from autistic individuals and culture and that has helped a lot. But most of all, at the root of us, is our love, and our ability to grow and learn together. Our simple act of touch has become integral: it tells the other person that the love is still there.

42

Meeting our needs in a neurodiverse marriage

*Jayne Johnston, blogger at https://squarepeggee.
blogspot.com, inclusive education professional and
lover of: being outside; being upside down; and dancing*

When asked to comment on the difference being autistic
makes in a relationship, I was going to plough in on the
obvious communication issue of misunderstandings
due to different use of language, different interpret-
ations and expectations, forgetting that people can't
read your mind (or understand unless you spell it out,
and this is both ways [in] most of my relationships –
people have to spell it out for me and I for them!) and
so on. And some of the ways we try and get round
these (e.g. hijacking the moments when my brain is
feeling communicative so I can tell my husband stuff.
Or trying to tell him that the question "How are you?"
or "How was your day?" makes me inexplicably angry,
and yet reminding myself to ask it to him, because it is
a good thing for people who aren't me!).

But instead! I want to talk about differing needs for
interaction and alone time. It's such a massive issue for
me. I can't get my arousal levels down to zero unless
I have what we really all define as excessive amounts
of time on my own (although I have been encouraged
to look at rephrasing the story I tell myself here!).
Preferably in an empty house. This can be upsetting for
my husband because he thinks he's done something
wrong, or that because I need time away from him that
it's him I have a problem with. It's not, it's just that
he's a human being and therefore I cannot be with him
without my stress levels increasing. It doesn't mean
I don't enjoy spending time with him, but it's just the
same as the general social battery or spoon theory.

Everything I do costs me, whether I enjoy it or not. So me saying I can't do something or that I need recovery time says absolutely nothing about the quality of the thing being done or my wish to do it, simply about the status of my capacity for 'stuff'.

If we can both learn not to judge ourselves or each other on that, things become much less stressful, and this goes for friendships too.

I now have a sensory cave for time alone, and spend two nights a week in a different bed. That hopefully gives him better quality interaction when we are together as I am more relaxed and not worrying about being able to get alone time. I'm currently working part-time, which drops our income but means my mental health is better so we can be more alive. He is being referred for carer support to see if that will help his wellbeing as he supports me. We try and talk clearly when something is bothering us and work through the emotions involved and how we can move forward. We try to recognise that I (or he) can need something and he (and/or I!) can be sad about it. Both of these things can be true, and that is OK.

It's hard to meet the needs of both partners in a relationship that crosses a neurodiverse divide, and that's something we're really still exploring, but determined to work towards. I won't accept him doing what I did for so many years of my life (not only in marriage) and masking true needs from himself or me. It only leads to decline in mental health, but awareness, understanding and accommodation can improve everyone's wellbeing.

21 Reflection: recognising the impossibility of change was crucial

This whole book echoes itself time and time again. Eleven-year-old me set out to not be autistic and 'achieved' her goal by the age of 17. In my adult life, I have formed a succession of committed relationships (two of which I have told you about here). Each has failed for similar reasons. Each time I decided that the next time it would be okay: the next time, I would not be autistic.

This time I got married, confident that because I *knew* I was autistic, and my husband knew it too, it would be okay. But it turns out the difficulties are not caused by whether you know you are autistic or not, the difficulties are caused by the translation error between autistic and neurotypical ways of thinking and being. Whether we know about them or not, those differences are still there. Even as I wrote my celebratory photoblog posts documenting how we were overcoming those barriers, I was walking down the same road I have been down so many times before: I was still essentially planning on not being autistic.

The journey I described in Chapter 3 is not the passive act of sitting on a train and being transported to the next stop. I have mapped the line, but have to propel myself along it.

However, something has changed.

I have avoided writing this book for years. I have built up the notes, built up the research, made the connections needed to write it, but never actually sat down to write.

My excuse was always that it was too complicated, that I did not have a big enough chunk of time to dedicate to it. And then in 2020, the global COVID-19 Pandemic hit, and as a pregnant woman, whose pregnancy was considered high risk, I began to 'isolate' a week before the UK went into lockdown. Isolating meant that I no longer went out to work. I no longer went out at all. Everything in my life stopped, with two exceptions: seeing my son, and seeing my husband.

I no longer had the excuse of there not being enough time to write. I sat down to write, but although I have written six books before, I could not write this one. Writer's block, I concluded. Ignoring the truth behind all my excuses: that I was not avoiding writing the book because I did not have enough time; I was avoiding it because I did not want to recognise how little progress I had made along the journey I would set out in its pages.

Against the blank backdrop of lockdown and pregnancy, it was easier to see the effect of autism on my life. My pre-lockdown life would have contained a million different activities in a day, and I would not have known which of them, if any, caused me to feel a certain way or react in a certain way. But in lockdown, days were sparse and simple and it was very clear to see the cause-and-effect links between certain activities and certain responses.

I was unable to get away from my husband on actual trains (not the metaphorical train journeys I have written about here), as was the routine of my working week prior to lockdown, and unable to get away from the reality of my autism. Without the travel involved in my job, I had no escape from the realities of being in a relationship and I had no excuse not to tackle the book.

The book and lockdown have conspired to rub my nose firmly in who I am, for better or for worse. I have not reached acceptance through desire, or even willingness, it has been an act of submission. Here in lockdown, it is inescapable. Here in this book, it is inescapable. I am autistic, and strategise as I might to be different, to learn a new way, to cope better next time, I remain autistic.

At the start of lockdown, my husband and I both wondered how I would cope with so much time spent together. Around us we witnessed different relationships react to the pressures of the time in different ways. I found that with nothing else pressing on my time, all of my energy could be spent looking at the reality of myself and my situation. For once, I was not spending this energy on trying to change it but just on trying to understand it. I was just looking at it and realising it was real.

Subtly, without escape, things seemed to change. The pressure of sharing the space eased. I was no longer cowed by his looking, from time to time I would notice it and comment and he would remove his gaze from me. This greater understanding of the subtleties of the spectrum has happened to him too, he has had time to notice the almost mystical difference a clear worksurface can make to the sanity of his wife.

I know that if our marriage survives it will not be because I learned to be different. I think quite probably if our marriage survives, it will be because he is different from other partners in his approach to me, in what he needs from me, and in what he loves me for. Part of that difference, but not all of it, is that he knows I am autistic.

How much more different would things be if I shifted from a forced acceptance of autism to embracing an autistic identity?

22   To be identified is our pride

Identity is a strange thing. A person can have a sense of self, a sense of who they are, of their own individuality, but not feel themselves to have an identity. In seeking an identity, we look to put words to our very personal, individual, sense of who we truly are.

There is something oxymoronic about this search for a means to state our identity, in that in seeking to define that which is deeply personal, we use words that correspond with collectives. For example: I am a woman, I am a mother, I am a wife. Each of these elements of myself is shared with a multitude of other people and I am not the same as those people. But perhaps if I gather up enough of these designators, I can draw a Venn diagram of words that describe me. If I had the right words, that small overlapping section in the middle, the part for which there really are no words apart from 'I' or 'Me', would be as close to defined as it could ever be.

For me to attempt to draw a Venn diagram of self without reference to my neurodivergent nature would be an impossible task. My 'I' cannot be defined without that claiming of autistic identity. I am autistic. It is not my whole identity, because I am also all of those other things too, and more: I am a friend, a mother, a wife, a sister, a daughter, I am a woman, I am white, I am educated, and so on. But my identity as autistic is crucial to the definition of the whole; it is the identity that colours all the others.

Were I to try and define myself, by drawing that Venn diagram, and miss out one of the other designators that describe who I am, the impact would not be the same as missing out the descriptor: autistic. If I say, "I am a wife, a sister, a woman" (but

I forget to mention I am someone's daughter) and I say, "I am autistic", the colour of that central section will be broadly accurate with the sense of self I hold inside. But if I say, "I am a wife, a sister, a woman, and a daughter" and leave out autistic, the colour of that central piece will be a blur, I could be anyone: I am undefined. Though each of the aspects of self I have mentioned is genuinely a part of who I am, they are not definitive of my self in the way that autism is. The word autism came originally from the Greek word 'autos' meaning self; autism is inherent to my self.

Identity serves both a public and private function in our lives:

> Privately if we have a sense of our own identity that bolsters our sense of self, it is protective of our essential being, of who we are. It is good for our wellbeing.
> Publicly having a sense of self enables us to use defining labels to tell others who we are. I can choose to state, "I am autistic", and in doing so get as close as I can to telling someone who I truly am. In this there is the potential to be known, to be understood, and to belong to a group. In stating an identity there is the possibility for an isolated life to become a connected one. To have an identity is a powerful thing personally and publicly.

The struggle for those currently looking to claim an autistic identity as a definition of self is that the term we reach for does not always hold firm. To cite autistic as definitive of identity, the word needs to be strong, like a handrail you grab when trying to stand unaided.

As I write, I am heavily pregnant and, in my day-to-day life currently I frequently bemoan the lack of grab handles around the house. If I could just reach out and grab something sturdy, I could get to my feet unaided, stand by myself. 'Autistic' is not well defined, not well understood, it is an unsteady handle, hard to right oneself against. But it gets stronger the more people use it, the more people articulate it, the more people put their name to it.

When I say, "I am a woman", there is a broad understanding of what that means. This understanding is fairly solid, challenged at its social edges by gender fluidity and its medical edges by people who are born with physical differences that make biological sex difficult to assign, but broadly speaking, I can expect everyone to understand what I mean by the term 'woman'. The same is true for 'wife' or ' sister'. But it is not true for 'autistic'.

When I say, "I am autistic", what do I expect people will think I mean by that word? They might be aware of their own lack of insight and ask me what it means. Their awareness of their lack of knowledge would be refreshing, but in asking me to define it whilst taking away *the* word that defines my experience of self, they are likely to leave me somewhat stuck.

When I say, "I am autistic", people might assume I am the same, or claiming to be the same as another autistic person they know or have heard about. They may have a fixed view of what autism is that does not include me. They may deny my identity, or they may take my declaration to be evidence that I am like the person in their minds, and not like the self in my mind.

My first experience of saying "I am autistic" was being told I should have used a different word – not 'autistic'. In other experiences you have read about in this book, the responses I received to tentative declarations of this identity have been direct denials: "No, you are not."

My experience of claiming identity has been one of not being able to, of having to explain and defend the identity I am attempting to own. And as has been reflected on in sections 2.6 and 3.5, and many other places within this book, the place where I encounter prejudice most uncomfortably is within my own mind.

When I think "I am autistic", the first thing my mind leaps to do is defend itself against itself. What right have I to say this? What right to even whisper it inside my own head? Am I autistic? When the response comes, there is no strength in the "I am" statement even within myself.

When I say, "I am autistic", I do not actually get to declare an identity, because there is not yet a socially, culturally, recognised autistic identity. You can see this lack in my own struggles to get off the train at the final stop (see section 3.6): What is it? Where is it? How can I disembark if I cannot perceive the place I am meant to be at?

All through this book, I have drawn parallels between autistic experience and the experience of other minority groups: women,

LGBTQ+ people, people from different races and religions and so on. I have been careful to point out at every juncture that these are parallels, not equivalents. The manifestations of discrimination that each group experiences are not the same; the lived experiences are not the same. Our particular battles, fights and struggles are not the same as theirs have been. Yes, there is a communality to what we all fight for: recognition, rights, justice and so on, but the particular nature of each fight is a reflection of the identity and experiences of the group fighting.

I think something strange has happened in our reaching for autistic identity, that has not happened with these other groups. I think that somewhat ironically the reason for this difference lies within the experience of autism itself. Autistics looking to claim identity as autistics are often people accustomed to having to appear to not be autistic. Part of the experience of autism is masking. Not that every autistic person masks, this is a spectrum experience, just that masking is a huge part of what we, collectively, have experienced. So here we stand – a group of people skilled at appearing like other people. And what have we done as we have pushed for our own identity?

Have we forged our own pathway to identity? Or have we adopted the pathway of another group? Have our masking skills gathered up what we know of claiming identity from groups we have seen do this before and placed what they do on us? Are we masking our way to claiming identity?

I think there is an argument to be made that in looking to claim their identity, the autistic community as a whole has adopted the LGBTQ+ community's approach to recognition. We have Autistic Pride events, mirroring Gay Pride, we 'come out' as autistic, mirroring the gay experience of coming out. I have even seen people refer to 'spectrum-dar', a reference to 'gaydar' – the supposed ability of LGBTQ+ people to spot each other in public even when no markers of sexuality are displayed.

It is true that there are many, many parallels to be drawn, but the direct adoption of one community's experience by another has drawbacks for both communities. In saying our experience is like theirs, we take away the unique elements on both sides, which is disrespectful to the LGBTQ+ community (an inadvertent, not intentional disrespect) and diminishing to the autistic community (as aspects of our experience are lost).

If we look back at the communities from which we have drawn insight, there is often one word that defines what they fought for:

> The Power fought for by the black community is a response to lives lived under the control of other authorities.
>
> The Rights of the women's movement is in response to lives lived without those rights: voting rights, reproductive rights etc.
>
> The Pride of the LGBTQ+ movement is in response to the shame that has been so foisted upon them historically.

Of course, as autistics we want power and agency over our lives, and we experience the lack of those things. We want rights, and are denied them. And we are proud to be autistic and reject the shaming notions that say to be so is defective. But these things are not what our particular, personal fight is about. They are not definitive of us.

Our fight is about identity itself. It is about the self that is inherent in autism.

When I say, "I am autistic", that statement does not currently carry the identifying clout that I wish it did.

How can I change the world so that it does?

I think that change is achieved in action: it is done in the doing: when I state publicly that "I am autistic"...

Even though those words do not hold the meaning I wish they did.

Even though I will be misunderstood.

Even though the act that I reach for to bolster my self-esteem and strengthen my sense of self may instead put me in a position where I am made vulnerable.

If I state, in spite of all these risks, "I am autistic", I put a name and a face to the identity.

In identifying myself publicly, I contribute to an understanding of autistic identity. I help to create the meaning the word is owed: the meaning it has within ourselves. The meaning held within that mass of collected identities, all the other people whose central component to their Venn diagram of self is definitively coloured by the same colour as my own. When we can claim *that* identity, then that will be our power, the source of our rights, and the source of our pride in who we are.

We move towards that world through individual acts of identification.

I imagine a great mass of people standing together and stating, "I am autistic." Their variety, their weirdness, their ordinariness, their difference, their very presence would describe the spectrum.

We want to be known, to be recognised, accepted, understood, but most of all we want to be able to claim the identity that is ours. We want that sense of self. In being identified, in identifying ourselves, we build that identity. Collectively stated, "I am autistic" would have the meaning it warrants.

Being identified is our pride.

In this book, I have exposed to you some of the most private aspects of my life, I have put myself on these pages, shown you the messy workings of my brain, it is not my whole life by any means, but what is here is very much me and exposing it makes me very vulnerable. Here I am ... and:

"I am autistic."

Autistic from the Greek 'autos', meaning self.[292]

(Now the Avicii[96] earworm I mentioned in 11.2.1, which previously just described wanting to be woken up, completes itself. It is funny how parts of your brain know things before you do. The final two lines describe the surprise of finding yourself when you did not know you were lost. Capturing, perfectly for me, my experience of discovering autistic identity.)

Bibliography

1. Bonnello, C. (2018) 11,521 people answered this autism survey. Warning: the results may challenge you. Autistic Not Weird. Accessed online on 2/7/20 at https://autisticnotweird. com/2018survey/
2. McCann, L. (2017) Why I am changing my language about autism. Reach Out ASC. Accessed online on 2/7/ 2020 at www.reachoutasc.com/blog/why-i-m-changing-my-language-about-autism-1
3. Milton, D. (2017) Difference versus disability: Implications of characterisation of autism for education and support. In R. Jordan (ed.), *The Sage Handbook of Autism and Education*. London, UK: SAGE.
4. Sparrow, M. (2017) Labels are valuable tools. Thinking Person's Guide to Autism. Accessed online on 2/7/20 at www. thinkingautismguide.com/2017/11/labels-are-valuable-tools.html
5. Identity-First Autistic (n.d.) Autistic is not a dirty word. Accessed online on 2/7/20 at www.identityfirstautistic.org/
6. Rose, K. (2017) I do not HAVE autism. The Autistic Advocate. Accessed online on 2/7/20 at https://theautisticadvocate. com/2017/10/i-do-not-have-autism/
7. Jess at Diary of a Mom (2012) Person first: An evolution in thinking. Thinking Person's Guide to Autism. Accessed online on 2/7/20 at www.thinkingautismguide.com/2012/ 07/person-first-evolution-in-thinking.html
8. Autistic UK CIC (2020) Identity-first language. Autistic UK CIC. Accessed online on 2/7/20 at https://autisticuk.org/ resources/identity-first-language/
9. Brown, L. (2011a) Identity-first language. ASAN. Accessed online on 2/7/20 at https://autisticadvocacy.org/about-asan/identity-first-language/

10. Brown, L. (2011b) Identity and hypocrisy: A second argument against person- first language. Autistic Hoya. Accessed online on 2/7/20 at www.autistichoya.com/2011/11/identity-and-hypocrisy-second-argument.html

11. Sinclair, J. (1999) Why I dislike "person first" language. Accessed online on 2/7/20 at http://web.archive.org/web/20090210190652/http://web.syr.edu/~jisincla/person_first.htm

12. Gernsbacher, M. A. (2017) Editorial perspective: The use of person-first language in scholarly writing may accentuate stigma. *Journal of Child Psychology and Psychiatry, and Allied Disciplines*, 58(7), 859–861. https://doi.org/10.1111/jcpp.12706

13. Hazlett, H., Gu, H., Munsell, B., Kim, S. H., Styler, M., Wolff, J. J. et al. (2017) Early brain development in infants at high risk for autism spectrum disorder. *Nature*, 542, 348–351. https://doi.org/10.1038/nature21369

14. Courchesne, E., Mouton, P. R., Calhoun, M. E., Semendeferi, K., Ahrens-Barbeau, C., Hallet, M. J. et al. (2011) Neuron number and size in prefrontal cortex of children with autism. *JAMA*, 306(18), 2001–2010. DOI: 10.1001/jama.2011.1638 Accessed online on 2/7/20 at https://jamanetwork.com/journals/jama/article-abstract/1104609

15. Sparks, B. F., Friedman, S. D., Shaw, D. W., Aylward, E. H., Echelard, D., Artru, A. A. et al. (2002) Brain structural abnormalities in young children with autism spectrum disorder. *Neurology*, 59(2), 184–192. DOI: 10.1212/WNL.59.2.184

16. Maximo, J. O. & Kana, R. K. (2019) Aberrant "deep connectivity" in autism: A cortico-subcortical functional connectivity magnetic resonance imaging study. *Autism Research*, 12(3), 384–400. DOI: 10.1002/aur.2058

17. Holiga, Š., Hipp, J. F., Chatham, C. H., Garces, P., Spooren, W., D'Ardhuy, X. L. et al. (2019) Patients with autism spectrum disorders display reproducible functional connectivity alterations. *Science Translational Medicine*, 11(481). DOI: 10.1126/scitranslmed.aat9223

18. Dartmouth (2018) Autism: A view from neuroscience – a CCN public lecture. Given by Dr Caroline Robertson. Accessed online on 3/7/20 at www.youtube.com/watch?v=2__A_Mb0V0g&list=FLvywTRPU1xuE6-wqYqTdoqw

19. Ouimet, T., Foster, N. E., Tryfon, A. & Hyde, K. L. (2012) Auditory-musical processing in autism spectrum disorders: A review of behavioral and brain imaging studies. *Annals of the New York Academy of Sciences*, 1252, 325–331. https://doi.org/10.1111/j.1749-6632.2012.06453.x

20. Lai, G., Pantazatos, S. P., Schneider, H. & Hirsch, J. (2012) Neural systems for speech and song in autism. *Brain: A Journal of Neurology*, 135(3), 961–975. https://doi.org/ 10.1093/brain/awr335 Accessed online on 2/7/20 at www. ncbi.nlm.nih.gov/pmc/articles/PMC3286324/

21. Fu, L., Wang, Y., Fang, H., Xiao, X., Xiao, T., Li, Y. et al. (2020) Longitudinal study of brain asymmetries in autism and developmental delays aged 2–5 years. *Neuroscience*, 432, 137–149. https://doi.org/10.1016/j.neuroscience. 2020.02.028

22. Kobayashi, A., Yokota, S., Takeuchi, H., Asano, K., Asano, M., Sassa, Y. et al. (2020) Increased grey matter volume of the right superior temporal gyrus in healthy children with autistic cognitive style: A VBM study. *Brain and Cognition*, 139, 105514. https://doi.org/10.1016/j.bandc.2019.105514

23. Yildiz, G. Y., Vilsten, J. S., Millard, A. S. & Chouinard, P. A. (2020) Grey-matter thickness of the left but not the right primary visual area correlates with autism traits in typically developing adults. *Journal of Autism and Developmental Disorders*. https://doi.org/10.1007/s10803-020-04553-w

24. Fouquet, M., Traut, N., Beggiato, A., Delorme, R., Bourgeron, T. & Toro, R. (2019) Increased contrast of the grey-white matter boundary in the motor, visual and auditory areas in autism spectrum disorders. DOI: 10.1101/750117

25. Oztan, O., Garner, J. P., Partap, S., Sherr, E. H., Hardan, A. Y., Farmer, C. et al. (2018) Cerebrospinal fluid vasopressin and symptom severity in children with autism. *Annals of Neurology*, 84(4), 611–615. https://doi.org/10.1002/ ana.25314

26. Tareen, R. S. & Kamboj, M. K. (2012) Role of endocrine factors in autistic spectrum disorders. *Pediatric Clinics of North America*, 59, 75–88. Accessed online on 2/7/20 at www. pediatric.theclinics.com/article/S0031-3955(11)00148 -9/pdf

27. Mariscal, M. G., Oztan, O., Rose, S. M., Libove, R. A., Jackson, L. P., Sumiyoshi, R. D. et al. (2019) Blood oxytocin concentration positively predicts contagious yawning behavior in children with autism spectrum disorder. *Autism Research*, 12, 1156–1161. DOI: 10.1002/aur.2135

28. Hadwin, J. A., Lee, E., Kumsta, R., Cortese, S. & Kovshoff, H. (2019) Cortisol awakening response in children and adolescents with autism spectrum disorder: A systematic review and meta-analysis. *Evidence-Based Mental Health*, 22, 118–124.

29. Buckley, A. W., Rodriguez, A. J., Jennison, K., Buckley, J., Thurm, A., Sato, S. et al. (2010) Rapid eye movement sleep percentage in children with autism compared with children with developmental delay and typical development. *Archives of Pediatrics & Adolescent Medicine*, 164(11), 1032–1037. https://doi.org/10.1001/archpediatrics.2010.202

30. Cohen, S., Conduit, R., Lockley, S. W., Rajaratnam, S. M. & Cornish, K. M. (2014) The relationship between sleep and behavior in autism spectrum disorder (ASD): A review. *Journal of Neurodevelopmental Disorders*, 6(1), 44. https://doi.org/10.1186/1866-1955-6-44

31. Thirumalai, S. S., Shubin, R. A. & Robinson, R. (2002) Rapid eye movement sleep behavior disorder in children with autism. *Journal of Child Neurology*, 17(3), 173–178. https://doi.org/10.1177/088307380201700304

32. Pérez Velázquez, J. L. & Galán, R. F. (2013) Information gain in the brain's resting state: A new perspective on autism. *Frontiers in Neuroinformatics*. DOI: 10.3389/fninf.2013.00037 Accessed online on 2/7/20 at www.frontiersin.org/articles/10.3389/fninf.2013.00037/full

33. Hahamy, A., Behrmann, M. & Malach, R. (2015) The idiosyncratic brain: Distortion of spontaneous connectivity patterns in autism spectrum disorder. *Nature Neuroscience*, 18(2), 302–309. https://doi.org/10.1038/nn.3919 Accessed online on 3/7/20 at www.cmu.edu/dietrich/behrmannlab/Publications/nn.3919.pdf

34. Folstein, S. & Rutter, M. (1977) Infantile autism: A genetic study of 21 twin pairs. *Journal of Child Psychology and Psychiatry*, 18, 297–321. DOI: 10.1111/j.1469-7610.1977.tb00443.x

35. Volkmar, F. R., Paul, R., Rogers, S. J., Pelphrey, K. A., Rutter, M. & Thapar, A. (2014) Genetics of autism spectrum disorders. In F. R. Volkmar, R. Paul, S. J. Rogers & K. A. Pelphrey (eds), *Handbook of Autism and Pervasive Developmental Disorders* (4th edition). DOI: 10.1002/9781118911389.hautc17

36. Silberman, S. (2015) *NeuroTribes: The Legacy of Autism and the Future of Neurodiversity*. New York: Avery, an imprint of Penguin Random House.

37. Acker, F. (2005) Autism and engineers – Is there a connection? *Ingenia*, 25. Accessed online on 2/7/20 at www.ingenia.org.uk/Ingenia/Articles/b2bb10a9-1d0b-445b-b690-865ff2abf553

38. Baron-Cohen, S., Wheelwright, S., Stott, C., Bolton, P. & Goodyer, I. (1997) Is there a link between engineering and

autism? *Autism*, 1(1), 101–109. https://doi.org/10.1177/1362361397011010

39. Baron-Cohen, S. (2006) The hyper-systemizing, assortative mating theory of autism. *Progress in Neuro-Psychopharmacology & Biological Psychiatry*, 30, 865–872. DOI: 10.1016/j.pnpbp.2006.01.010

40. Mazefsky, C. A., Herrington, J., Siegel, M., Scarpa, A., Maddox, B. B., Scahill, L. et al. (2013) The role of emotion regulation in autism spectrum disorder. *Journal of the American Academy of Child and Adolescent Psychiatry*, 52(7), 679–688.

41. Milton, D. E. (2019) Beyond tokenism: Autistic people in autism research. *The Psychologist*. Accessed online on 18/6/20 via https://kar.kent.ac.uk/76022/

42. Autism CRC (2020) Autism CRC: About us. Accessed online on 3/7/20 at www.autismcrc.com.au/about-us

43. Nicolaidis, C., Raymaker, D., Kapp, S. K., Baggs, A., Ashkenazy, E., McDonald, K. et al. (2019) The AASPIRE practice-based guidelines for the inclusion of autistic adults in research as co-researchers and study participants. *Autism: The International Journal of Research and Practice*, 23(8), 2007–2019. https://doi.org/10.1177/1362361319830523

44. ASAN (2016) ASAN expresses concern over new autism research funding numbers. Accessed online on 2/7/20 at https://autisticadvocacy.org/2016/04/asan-expresses-concern-over-new-autism-research-funding-numbers/

45. Levinson, B. (Director) (1988) *Rain man* [Film]. Guber-Peters Company.

46. Rose, K. (2020) Autism Acceptance, fake news and inconvenient truths. The Autistic Advocate. Accessed online on 12/6/20 at https://theautisticadvocate.com/2020/04/in-lieu-of-tosh-here-are-some-facts/

47. Enacting Autism and Inclusion (2019) Re Storying Autism research team: Estée Klar. Accessed online on 25/6/20 at www.restoryingautism.com/video-gallery/estee-klar-untitled

48. FINAL_Autism and Inclusion Documentary_August 25th 2017 (2017) Clip from Estée Klar's film, added by Re Storying Autism. Accessed online on 25/6/20 at https://vimeo.com/237504887

49. Berkowitz, L. (2017) Interview with Paula Durbin-Westby. Autistic Women & Nonbinary Network, April 27. Accessed online on 25/6/20 at https://awnnetwork.org/interview-with-paula-Durbin-westby/

50. Harris, P. (2017) Interviewing the founder of Autism Acceptance Month. Assistiveware Blog. Accessed online on 25/6/20 at www.assistiveware.com/blog/interviewing-the-founder-of-autism-acceptance-month

51. Cooper, K., Smith, L. G. E. & Russell, A. (2017) Social identity, self-esteem, and mental health in autism. *European Journal of Social Psychology*, 47, 844–854. DOI: 10.1002/ejsp.2297

52. Rose, K. (2019) An autistic identity. The Autistic Advocate. Accessed online on 1/7/20 at https://theautisticadvocate.com/2019/03/an-autistic-identity/

53. National Autistic Society (2016) *The Autism Employment Gap: Too Much Information in the Workplace*. Available at www.basw.co.uk/resources/autism-employment-gap-too-much-information-workplace

54. ONS (2016) *UK Labour Market: Dec 2016 Estimates of Employment, Unemployment, Economic Inactivity and Other Employment-Related Statistics for the UK*. Accessed online on 28/6/20 at www.ons.gov.uk/employmentandlabourmarket/peopleinwork/employmentandemployeetypes/bulletins/uklabourmarket/dec2016

55. ONS (2020) *UK Labour Market: June 2020 Estimates of Employment, Unemployment, Economic Inactivity and Other Employment-Related Statistics for the UK*. Accessed online on 28/6/20 at www.ons.gov.uk/employmentandlabourmarket/peopleinwork/employmentandemployeetypes/bulletins/uklabourmarket/june2020

56. Kirby, A. (2020b) Where have all the girls gone? Neurodiversity and females. Do-IT Solutions. Accessed online at www.fenews.co.uk/featured-article/42884-where-have-all-the-girls-gone-missed-misunderstood-or-misdiagnosed

57. Gotham, K., Marvin, A. R., Taylor, J. L., Warren, Z., Anderson, C. M., Law, P. A. et al. (2015) Characterizing the daily life, needs, and priorities of adults with autism spectrum disorder from Interactive Autism Network data. *Autism*, 19(7), 794–804. https://doi.org/10.1177/1362361315583818

58. Pellicano, E., Dinsmore, A. & Charman, T. (2014) What should autism research focus upon? Community views and priorities from the United Kingdom. *Autism*, 18(7), 756–770. https://doi.org/10.1177/1362361314529627

59. Howlin, P., Goode, S., Hutton, J. & Rutter, M. (2004) Adult outcome for children with autism. *Journal of Child Psychology and Psychiatry*, 45, 212–229. DOI: 10.1111/j.1469-7610.2004.00215.x

60. Howlin, P. & Moss, P. (2012) Adults with autism spectrum disorders. *The Canadian Journal of Psychiatry*, 57(5), 275–283. https://doi.org/10.1177/070674371205700502

61. Hendricks, D. (2010) Employment and adults with autism spectrum disorders: Challenges and strategies for success. *Journal of Vocational Rehabilitations*, 32, 125–134. DOI: 10.3233/JVR-2010-0502 Accessed online on 28/6/20 at https://worksupport.com/documents/JVRautismHendricks.pdf

62. Milton, D. (2018) The double empathy problem: Practical implications. In *Scottish Autism Conference: Innovation in Autism Practice: The Future Is Here, 14 November 2019, Glasgow, UK*. Accessed online at www.scottishautismconference.org/assets/pdf/presentations/Keynote_2_-_Double_Empathy_Problem_-_Dr_Damian_Milton.pdf

63. Roslin, L. (2019) 1/4 of UK employees bullied at work. Accessed online on 28/6/20 at https://smeloans.co.uk/bullying-in-the-workplace-statistics-uk/

64. TUC (2015) Nearly a third of people are bullied at work, says TUC. Accessed online on 28/6/20 at www.tuc.org.uk/news/nearly-third-people-are-bullied-work-says-tuc

65. Warnick, J. (2016) Kyle Schwaneke: Unique Microsoft hiring program opens more doors to people with autism. Microsoft. Accessed online on 28/6/20 at https://news.microsoft.com/stories/people/kyle-schwaneke.html

66. Twaronite, K. (2019) How neurodiversity is driving innovation from unexpected places. EY. Accessed online on 28/6/20 at www.ey.com/en_us/diversity-inclusiveness/how-neurodiversity-is-driving-innovation-from-unexpected-places

67. EY Americas (2018) Do great minds always think alike? EY. Accessed online on 28/6/20 at www.ey.com/en_us/workforce/do-great-minds-always-think-alike

68. Neurodiversity Hub (2020) The Neurodiversity Hub. Accessed online on 9/7/20 at www.neurodiversityhub.org/home

69. Untapped (2020) The facts. Accessed online on 9/7/20 at www.untapped-group.com/#statistics

70. APPG Women and Work (2019) *Inclusivity and Intersectionality: Toolkit and Annual Report 2019*. Accessed online on 28/6/20 at https://connectpa.co.uk/wp-content/uploads/2020/02/Women-and-work-Annual-report-2019-A4.pdf

71. NASEN (2016) Girls and autism: Flying under the radar. Available at https://nasen.org.uk/resources/girls-and-autism-flying-under-radar

72. Kirby, A. (2020a) Where have all the girls gone? Missed, misunderstood or misdiagnosed? FE News. Accessed online on 26/6/20 at www.fenews.co.uk/featured-article/42884-where-have-all-the-girls-gone-missed-misunderstood-or-misdiagnosed

73. Constantino, J. N. & Charman, T. (2012) Gender bias, female resilience, and the sex ratio in autism. *Journal of the American Academy of Child and Adolescent Psychiatry*, 51(8), 756–758.

74. Kreiser, N. L. & White, S. W. (2014) ASD in females: Are we overstating the gender difference in diagnosis? *Clinical Child and Family Psychology Review*, 17(1), 67–84.

75. Goldman, S. (2014) Sex, gender and the diagnosis of autism – A biosocial view of the male preponderance. *Research in Autism Spectrum Disorders*, 7(6), 675–679.

76. Adamou, M., Johnson, M. & Alty, B. (2018) Autism Diagnostic Observation Schedule (ADOS) scores in males and females diagnosed with autism: A naturalistic study. *Advances in Autism*, 4, 49–55.

77. Wilson, C. E., Murphy, C. M., McAlonan, G., Robertson, D. M., Spain, D., Hayward, H. et al. (2016) Does sex influence the diagnostic evaluation of autism spectrum disorder in adults? *Autism*, 20, 808–819.

78. Nussbaum, N. L. (2012) ADHD and female specific concerns: A review of the literature and clinical implications. *Journal of Attention Disorders*, 16, 87–100.

79. Duvekot, J., van der Ende, J., Verhulst, F. C., Slappendel, G., van Daalen, E., Maras, A. et al. (2017) Factors influencing the probability of a diagnosis of autism spectrum disorder in girls versus boys. *Autism*, 21(6), 646–658.

80. Lai, M.-C. & Baron-Cohen, S. (2015) Identifying the lost generation of adults with autism spectrum conditions. *The Lancet Psychiatry*, 2(11), 1013–1027.

81. Hiller, R. M., Young, R. & Weber, N. (2014) Sex differences in autism spectrum disorder based on DSM-5 criteria: Evidence from clinician and teacher reporting. *Journal of Abnormal Child Psychology*, 42(8), 1381–1393. https://doi.org/10.1007/s10802-014-9881-x

82. Solomon, M., Miller, M., Taylor, S. L., Hinshaw, S. P. & Carter, C. S. (2012) Autism symptoms and internalizing psychopathology in girls and boys with autism spectrum disorders.

Journal of Autism and Developmental Disorders, 42(1), 48–59. https://doi.org/10.1007/s10803-011-1215-z

83. Autistic UK CIC (2020) About autism. Accessed online on 12/6/20 at https://autisticuk.org/resources/about-autism/

84. Baron-Cohen, S., Wheelwright, S., Skinner, R., Martin, J. & Clubley, E. (2001) The autism-spectrum quotient (AQ): Evidence from Asperger syndrome/high-functioning autism, males and females, scientists and mathematicians. *Journal of Autism and Developmental Disorders*, 31(1), 5–17.

85. Chamberlain, B., Kasari, C. & Rotheram-Fuller, E. (2007) Involvement or isolation? The social networks of children with autism in regular classrooms. *Journal of Autism and Developmental Disorders*, 37(2), 230–242.

86. Sedgewick, F., Hill, V., Yates, R., Pickering, L. & Pellicano, E. (2015) Gender differences in the social motivation and friendship experiences of autistic and nonautistic adolescents. *Journal of Autism and Developmental Disorders*, 46(4), 1297–1306.

87. Rowe, A. (2020) Understanding separation anxiety. Accessed online on 2/7/2020 at https://thegirlwiththecurlyhair.co.uk/2020/06/10/understanding-separation-anxiety/

88. Vance, T. (2019) 50 ways society gaslights and stonewalls autistic people. The NeuroClastic. Accessed online on 9/7/20 at https://neuroclastic.com/2019/05/24/ways-society-gaslights-autistics/

89. Memmott, A. (2015) Autism: Denials and 'gaslighting'. Ann's Autism Blogspot. Accessed online on 9/7/20 at http://annsautism.blogspot.com/2015/12/autism-denials-and-gaslighting.html

90. Kennedy, A. (2019) Autism and gaslighting – Joely Williams speaks on 'all things autism'. *Psychreg*. Accessed online on 9/7/20 at www.psychreg.org/autism-gaslighting/

91. Seventh Voice (2019) The gas-lighting of women and girls on the autism spectrum. Accessed online on 9/7/20 at https://seventhvoice.wordpress.com/2014/12/10/the-gas-lighting-of-women-and-girls-on-the-autism-spectrum/

92. Adams, D. (1979) *The Hitchhiker's Guide to the Galaxy*. London: Pan Books.

93. Greensfelder, A. and others (Executive Producer) (2007–) *Say yes to the dress* [TV series]. TLC.

94. Grace, J. & Salfield, C. (2017) Inclusion: For pity's sake. TEDx talk. Accessed on 20/8/20 at www.youtube.com/watch?v=_PbWFcVcaWQ

95. Griffiths, J. (Jem) (2004) Just a ride [Song]. On *Finally woken* [Album]. ATO Records/Crazy Wise Music.

96. Bergling, T. (Avicii), Einziger, M. & Blacc, A. (2013) Wake me up [Song]. On *True* [Album]. PRMD Music Lava Records/ Columbia Records/Sony Music Entertainment.

97. Asperger, H. (1944) Die autistisehen Psychopathen im Kindesalter. *Archiv für Psychiatrie und Nervenkrankheit*, 117, 76–136.

98. Kanner, L. (1943) Autistic disturbances of affective contact. *Nervous Child*, 2, 217–250.

99. Chapple, E. (2019) Diversity is the key to our survival: The Shoeness of a Shoe. TEDx talk. Accessed online on 1/7/20 at www.youtube.com/watch?v=DXBdiGUQ8Lw&feature=yo utu.be

100. Griffiths, S., Allison, C., Kenny, R., Holt, R., Smith, P. & Baron-Cohen, S. (2019) The Vulnerability Experiences Quotient (VEQ): A study of vulnerability, mental health and life satisfaction in autistic adults. *Autism Research*, 12(10), 1516–1528. DOI: 10.1002/aur.2162

101. Crane, L., Adams, F., Harper, G., Welch, J. & Pellicano, E. (2019) 'Something needs to change': Mental health experiences of young autistic adults in England. *Autism*, 23(2), 477–493.

102. Russell, A. J., Murphy, C. M., Wilson, E., Gillan, N., Brown, C., Robertson, D. M. et al. (2016) The mental health of individuals referred for assessment of autism spectrum disorder in adulthood: A clinic report. *Autism*, 20(5), 623–627. https://doi.org/10.1177/1362361315604271

103. Jones, L., Goddard, L., Hill, E. L., Henry, A. L. & Crane, L. (2014) Experiences of receiving a diagnosis of autism spectrum disorder: A survey of adults in the United Kingdom. *Journal of Autism and Developmental Disorders*, 44, 3033–3044. https://doi.org/10.1007/s10803-014-2161-3

104. Lake, J. K., Perry, A. & Lunsky, Y. (2014) Mental health services for individuals with high functioning autism spectrum disorder. *Autism Research and Treatment*, Article ID 502420. https://doi.org/10.1155/2014/502420

105. Berthoz, S., Lalanne, C., Crane, L. & Hill, E. (2013) Investigating emotional impairments in adults with autism spectrum disorders and the broader autism phenotype. *Psychiatry Research*, 208(3). https://doi.org/10.1016/j.psychres.2013.05.014

106. Strang, J. F., Kenworthy, L., Daniolos, P., Case, L., Wills, M. C., Martin, A. et al. (2012) Depression and anxiety symptoms in children and adolescents with autism spectrum disorders without intellectual disability. *Research in Autism Spectrum Disorders*, 6(1). https://doi.org/10.1016/j.rasd.2011.06.015

107. Skokauskas, N. & Gallagher, L. (2012) Mental health aspects of autistic spectrum disorders in children. *Journal of Intellectual Disability Research*, 56, 248–257. DOI: 10.1111/j.1365-2788.2011.01423.x

108. Lundström, S., Chang, Z., Kerekes, N., Gumpert, C. H., Råstam, M., Gillberg, C. et al. (2011) Autistic-like traits and their association with mental health problems in two nation-wide twin cohorts of children and adults. *Psychological Medicine*, 41(11), 2423–2433. https://doi.org/10.1017/S0033291711000377

109. Stewart, M. E., Barnard, L., Pearson, J., Hasan, R. & O'Brien, G. (2006) Presentation of depression in autism and Asperger syndrome: A review. *Autism*, 10(1), 103–116. https://doi.org/10.1177/1362361306062013

110. Barnhill, G. P. (2001) Social attributions and depression in adolescents with Asperger syndrome. *Focus on Autism and Other Developmental Disabilities*, 16(1), 46–53. https://doi.org/10.1177/108835760101600112

111. Rosenblatt, M. (2008) *I Exist: The Message from Adults with Autism in England*. London, UK: The National Autistic Society.

112. Licence, L., Oliver, C., Moss, J. & Richards, C. (2019) Prevalence and risk-markers of self-harm in autistic children and adults. *Journal of Autism and Developmental Disorders*. https://doi.org/10.1007/s10803-019-04260-1

113. Moseley, R., Gregory, N. J., Smith, P., Allison, C. & Baron-Cohen, S. (2019) A "choice", an "addiction", a way "out of the lost": Exploring self-injury in autistic people without intellectual disability. *Molecular Autism*, 10(1), 18.

114. Maddox, B. B., Trubanova, A. & White, S. W. (2017) Untended wounds: Non-suicidal self-injury in adults with autism spectrum disorder. *Autism*, 21(4), 412–422.

115. Croen, L. A., Zerbo, O. & Yinge, Q. (2015) The health status of adults on the autism spectrum. *Autism*, 19(7), 814–823.

116. Victor, S. E., Styer, D. & Washburn, J. J. (2015) Characteristics of nonsuicidal self-injury associated with suicidal ideation: Evidence from a clinical sample of youth. *Child and Adolescent Psychiatry and Mental Health*, 9(1), 20.

117. Owens, D., Horrocks, J. & House, A. (2002) Fatal and non-fatal repetition of self-harm: Systematic review. *The British Journal of Psychiatry*, 181(3), 193–199.

118. Conner, C. M., Golt, J., Righi, G., Shaffer, R., Siegel, M. & Mazefsky, C. A. (2020) A comparative study of suicidality and its association with emotion regulation impairment

in large ASD and US Census-matched samples. *Journal of Autism and Developmental Disorders.* https://doi.org/10.1007/s10803-020-04370-1

119. McCarthy, J., Chaplin, E., Forrester, A., Underwood, L., Hayward, H., Sabet, J. et al. (2020) Prisoners with neurodevelopmental difficulties: Vulnerabilities for mental illness and self- harm. *Criminal Behaviour and Mental Health*, 29(5–6), 308–320. https://doi.org/10.1002/cbm.2132

120. Pelton, M. K. & Cassidy, S. A. (2017) Are autistic traits associated with suicidality? A test of the interpersonal-psychological theory of suicide in a non-clinical young adult sample. *Autism Research*, 10, 1891–1904. DOI: 10.1002/aur.1828

121. Pelton, M. K., Crawford, H., Robertson, A. E., Rodgers, J., Baron-Cohen, S. & Cassidy, S. (2020) Understanding suicide risk in autistic adults: Comparing the interpersonal theory of suicide in autistic and non-autistic samples. *Journal of Autism and Developmental Disorders.* https://doi.org/10.1007/s10803-020-04393-8

122. Dow, D., Morgan, L., Hooker, J. L., Michaels, M. S., Joiner, T. E., Woods, J. et al. (2019) Anxiety, depression, and the interpersonal theory of suicide in a community sample of adults with autism spectrum disorder. *Archives of Suicide Research.* DOI: 10.1080/13811118.2019.1678537

123. Zahid, S. & Upthegrove, R. (2017) Suicidality in autistic spectrum disorders: A systematic review. *Crisis*, 38, 237–246.

124. Karakoç, D. S., Tutkunkardaş, M. D. & Mukaddes, N. M. (2016) Assessment of suicidality in children and adolescents with diagnosis of high functioning autism spectrum disorder in a Turkish clinical sample. *Neuropsychiatric Disease and Treatment*, 12, 2921–2926. DOI: 10.2147/NDT.S118304

125. Hirvikoski, T., Mittendorfer-Rutz, E., Boman, M., Larsson, H., Lichtenstein, P. & Bölte, S. (2016) Premature mortality in autism spectrum disorder. *British Journal of Psychiatry*, 208(3), 232–238. DOI: 10.1192/bjp.bp.114.160192

126. Segers, M. & Rawana, J. (2014) What do we know about suicidality in autism spectrum disorders? A systematic review. *Autism Research*, 7(4), 507–521. DOI: 10.1002/aur.1375

127. Mayes, S. D., Gorman, A. A. & Hillwig-Garcia, J. (2013) Suicide ideation and attempts in children with autism. *Research in Autism Spectrum Disorders*, 7(1), 109–119.

128. Storch, E. A., Sulkowski, M. L., Nadeau, J., Lewin, A. B., Arnold, E. B., Mutch, P. J. et al. (2013) The phenomenology

and clinical correlates of suicidal thoughts and behaviors in youth with autism spectrum disorders. *Journal of Autism and Developmental Disorders*, 43, 2450–2459. https://doi.org/10.1007/s10803-013-1795-x

129. Raja, M., Azzoni, A. & Frustaci, A. (2011) Autism spectrum disorders and suicidality. *Clinical Practice and Epidemiology in Mental Health*, 7, 97–105. https://doi.org/10.2174/1745017901107010097

130. Balfe, M. & Tantam, D. A (2010) Descriptive social and health profile of a community sample of adults and adolescents with Asperger syndrome. *BMC Research Notes*, 3, 300. https://doi.org/10.1186/1756-0500-3-300

131. Camm-Crosbie, L., Bradley, L., Shaw, R., Baron-Cohen, S. & Cassidy, S. (2018) 'People like me don't get support': Autistic adults' experiences of support and treatment for mental health difficulties, self-injury and suicidality. *Autism*. https://doi.org/10.1177/1362361318816053

132. Nicolaidis, C., Raymaker, D. M., Ashkenazy, E., McDonald, K. E., Dern, S., Baggs, A. E. et al. (2015) "Respect the way I need to communicate with you": Healthcare experiences of adults on the autism spectrum. *Autism*, 19(7), 824–831. https://doi.org/10.1177/1362361315576221

133. Raja, M. (2014) Suicide risk in adults with Asperger's syndrome. *The Lancet Psychiatry*, 1(2), 99–101.

134. Berthoz, S. & Hill, E. L. (2005) The validity of using self-reports to assess emotion regulation abilities in adults with autism spectrum disorder. *European Psychiatry*, 20, 291–298. DOI: 10.1016/j.eurpsy.2004.06.013

135. Heasman, B. & Gillespie, A. (2018) Perspective-taking is two-sided: Misunderstandings between people with Asperger's syndrome and their family members. *Autism*, 22(6), 740–750. https://doi.org/10.1177/1362361317708287

136. Milton, D., Heasman, B. & Sheppard, E. (2018) Double empathy. In: F. Volkmar (ed.), *Encyclopedia of Autism Spectrum Disorders*. New York: Springer.

137. Gernsbacher, M. A., Stevenson, J. L. & Dern, S. (2017) Specificity, contexts, and reference groups matter when assessing autistic traits. *PLoS ONE*, 12(2), e0171931.

138. Autism in Adulthood (2019) An expert discussion on autism and empathy. Moderator: Christina Nicolaidis. Participants: Damian Milton, Noah J. Sasson, Elizabeth (Lizzy) Sheppard and Melanie Yergeau. Accessed online on 18/6/20 at www.liebertpub.com/doi/10.1089/aut.2018.29000.cjn

139. Harkaway, N. (2017) *Gnonom*. London: William Heinemann.

140. Gernsbacher, M. A. & Yergeau, M. (2019) Empirical failures of the claim that autistic people lack a theory of mind. *Archives of Scientific Psychology*, 7(1), 102.

141. Usher, L. V., Burrows, C. A., Messinger, D. S. & Henderson, H. A. (2018) Metaperception in adolescents with and without autism spectrum disorder. *Journal of Autism and Developmental Disorders*, 48(2), 533–548. https://doi.org/10.1007/s10803-017-3356-1

142. Salt, M. (2019) *Deficits or Differences? A New Methodology for Studying Pragmatic Language in Autism Spectrum Disorder* (Doctoral thesis, University of Western Ontario, London, Canada).

143. Brewer, R., Biotti, F., Catmur, C., Press, C., Happé, F., Cook, R. et al. (2016) Can neurotypical individuals read autistic facial expressions? Atypical production of emotional facial expressions in autism spectrum disorders. *Autism Research: Official Journal of the International Society for Autism Research*, 9(2), 262–271. https://doi.org/10.1002/aur.1508

144. Milton, D. E. (2012) On the ontological status of autism: The 'double empathy problem'. *Disability & Society*, 27(6), 883–887. DOI: 10.1080/09687599.2012.710008

145. Fletcher-Watson, S., Adams, J. & Brook, K. (2018) Making the future together: Shaping autism research through meaningful participation. *Autism*. Accessed online on 18/6/20 at https://journals.sagepub.com/doi/pdf/10.1177/1362361318786721

146. Milton, D. E. (2014) Autistic expertise: A critical reflection on the production of knowledge in autism studies. *Autism*, 18(7), 794–802. DOI: 10.1177/1362361314525281

147. Sinclair, J. (1993) Don't mourn for us. Accessed on 10/11/2009 at www.autreat.com/dont_mourn.html. Cited by Milton (2012; see no. 144).

148. Hacking, I. (2009) Autistic autobiography. *Philosophical Transactions of the Royal Society: Biological Sciences*, 364(1522), 1467–1473. Cited by Milton (2012; see no. 144).

149. Dr Brett (2019) Double Empathy Series. Accessed on 18/6/20 at www.youtube.com/playlist?list=PLuUBsNTGvoBShmt0uH7VbCvW_fRDhz-Op

150. ASAN (2012) (updated 2020) Anti-filicide toolkit. Accessed on 4/6/20 at https://autisticadvocacy.org/wp-content/uploads/2015/01/ASAN-Anti-Filicide-Toolkit-Complete.pdf

151. Wikipedia (2020) Capital punishment for homosexuality. Accessed on 4/6/2020 at https://en.wikipedia.org/wiki/Capital_punishment_for_homosexuality

152. Eartharcher, L. (2017) Asperger's/autism and 'black-and-white thinking'. The Silent Wave. Accessed online on 29/7/20 at https://thesilentwaveblog.wordpress.com/2017/03/08/aspergers-autism-and-black-and-white-thinking/

153. Fisher, M. H. & Taylor, J. L. (2016) Let's talk about it: Peer victimization experiences as reported by adolescents with autism spectrum disorder. *Autism*, 20(4), 402–411. https://doi.org/10.1177/1362361315585948

154. Schroeder, J. H., Cappadocia, M. C., Bebko, J. M., Pepler, D. J. & Weiss, J. A. (2014) Shedding light on a pervasive problem: A review of research on bullying experiences among children with autism spectrum disorders. *Journal of Autism and Developmental Disorders*, 44(7), 1520–1534. DOI: 10.1007/s10803-013-2011-8

155. Cappadocia, M. C., Weiss, J. A. & Pepler, D. (2012) Bullying experiences among children and youth with autism spectrum disorders. *Journal of Autism and Developmental Disorders*, 42, 266–277. https://doi.org/10.1007/s10803-011-1241-x

156. Hoover, D. W. & Kaufman, J. (2018) Adverse childhood experiences in children with autism spectrum disorder. *Current Opinion in Psychiatry*, 31(2), 128–132. DOI: 10.1097/YCO.0000000000000390

157. Reid, B. (2011) *Great Expectations*. London, UK: The National Autistic Society.

158. Maïano, C., Normand, C., Salvas, M.-C., Moullec, G. & Aimé, A. (2015) Prevalence of school bullying among youth with autism spectrum disorders: A systematic review and meta-analysis. *Autism Research*, 9. DOI: 10.1002/aur.1568

159. Pearson, A., Rees, J. & Forster, S. (2020, March 16) "This was just how this friendship worked": Experiences of inter-personal victimisation in autistic and non-autistic adults. https://doi.org/10.31219/osf.io/amn6k https://osf.io/amn6k/

160. Simone, R. & Grandin, T. (2010) *Asperger's on the Job: Must-Have Advice for People with Asperger's or High Functioning Autism and their Employers, Educators, and Advocates*. Arlington, TX: Future Horizons.

161. Booth, J. (2014) Autism in the workplace. TUC. Accessed online on 13/6/20 at www.tuc.org.uk/sites/default/files/Autism.pdf

162. Healthed (2015) Professor Tony Attwood – Autism in females. Available at https://vimeo.com/122940958 (accessed 5/6/2020).

163. Yellow Ladybugs (n.d.) Are you concerned that your daughter isn't coping socially or emotionally? Common

traits [of autism] in girls. Accessed online on 2/7/20 at www.yellowladybugs.com.au/img/YLB_GirlTraits_A3.pdf

164. Chapman, R. (2017) We need to talk about the domestic abuse of autistic adults. Accessed online on 1/7/20 at https://medium.com/the-establishment/we-need-to-talk-about-the-domestic-abuse-of-autistic-adults-5df294504a13

165. Nicolaidis, C., Raymaker, D., McDonald, K., Dern, S., Boisclair, W. C., Ashkenazy, E. et al. (2013) Comparison of healthcare experiences in autistic and non-autistic adults: A cross-sectional online survey facilitated by an academic–community partnership. *Journal of General Internal Medicine*, 28, 761–769. https://doi.org/10.1007/s11606-012-2262-7

166. Unigwe, S., Buckley, C., Crane, L., Kenny, L., Remington, A. & Pellicano, E. (2017) GPs' confidence in caring for their patients on the autism spectrum: An online self-report study. *British Journal of General Practice*, 67(659), e445–E452. DOI: 10.3399/bjgp17X690449

167. Allely, C. S. (2013) Pain sensitivity and observer perception of pain in individuals with autistic spectrum disorder. *The Scientific World Journal*, Article ID 916178. https://doi.org/10.1155/2013/916178

168. Rattaz, C., Dubois, A., Michelon, C., Viellard, M., Poinso, F. & Baghdadli, A. (2013) How do children with autism spectrum disorders express pain? A comparison with developmentally delayed and typically developing children. *Pain*, 154(10), 2007–2013.

169. Tordjman, S., Anderson, G. M., Botbol, M., Brailly-Tabard, S., Perez-Diaz, F., Graignic, R. et al. (2009) Pain reactivity and plasma beta-endorphin in children and adolescents with autistic disorder. *PLoS ONE*, 4(8), e5289. https://doi.org/10.1371/journal.pone.0005289

170. Nader, R., Oberlander, T. F., Chambers, C. T. & Craig, K. D. (2004) Expression of pain in children with autism. *The Clinical Journal of Pain*, 20(2), 88–97. https://doi.org/10.1097/00002508-200403000-00005

171. Rydzewska, E., Hughes-McCormack, L. A., Gillberg, C., Henderson, A., Macintyre, C., Rintoul, J. et al. (2019) General health of adults with autism spectrum disorders: A whole country population cross-sectional study. *Research in Autism Spectrum Disorders*, 60, 59–66. https://doi.org/10.1016/j.rasd.2019.01.004

172. Weiss, J. A. & Fardella, M. A. (2018) Victimization and perpetration experiences of adults with autism. *Frontiers in Psychiatry*, 9, 203. https://doi.org/10.3389/fpsyt.2018.00203

173. Roberts, A. L., Koenen, K. C., Lyall, K., Robinson, E. B. & Weisskopf, M. G. (2015) Association of autistic traits in adulthood with childhood abuse, interpersonal victimization, and posttraumatic stress. *Child Abuse & Neglect*, 45, 135–142. Accessed online on 13/6/20 at www.sciencedirect.com/ science/article/abs/pii/S0145213415001283?via%3Dihub

174. National Autistic Society. (2014) *Careless*. London, UK: The National Autistic Society.

175. Van Heijst, B. F. & Geurts, H. M. (2015) Quality of life in autism across the lifespan: A meta-analysis. *Autism*, 19(2), 158–167. DOI: 10.1177/1362361313517053 Accessed online at https://pubmed.ncbi.nlm.nih.gov/24443331/

176. Hill, A. (2018) Autistic people angry at having to disclose diagnosis to DVLA even if driving not affected. *The Guardian*. Accessed online on 28/6/20 at www.theguardian.com/ society/2019/mar/03/autistic-people-angry-at-having-to-disclose-diagnosis-to-dvla-even-if-driving-not-affected

177. Urbano, M. R., Hartmann, K., Deutsch, S. I., Bondi Polychronopoulos, G. M. & Dorbin, V. (2013) Relationships, sexuality, and intimacy in autism spectrum disorders. In M. Fitzgerald (ed.), *Recent Advances in Autism Spectrum Disorders*. Vol. 1. Dublin: Trinity College Dublin. Accessed online on 11/6/20 at www.intechopen.com/books/ recent-advances-in-autism-spectrum-disorders-volume-i

178. Sevlever, M., Roth, M. E. & Gillis, J. M. (2013) Sexual abuse and offending in autism spectrum disorders. *Sexuality and Disability*, 31, 189–200. https://doi.org/10.1007/ s11195-013-9286-8

179. McDonnell, C. G., Boan, A. D., Bradley, C. C., Seay, K. D., Charles, J. M. & Carpenter L. A. (2019) Child maltreatment in autism spectrum disorder and intellectual disability: Results from a population-based sample. *Journal of Child Psychology and Psychiatry*, 60(5), 576–584. DOI: 10.1111/jcpp.12993

180. Murphy, N. A. & Elias, E. R. (2006) Sexuality of children and adolescents with developmental disabilities. *Pediatrics*, 118(1), 398–403. DOI: 10.1542/peds.2006-1115

181. Mandell, D. S., Walrath, C. M., Manteuffel, B., Sgro, G. & Pinto-Martin, J. A. (2005) The prevalence and correlates of abuse among children with autism served in comprehensive community-based mental health settings. *Child Abuse & Neglect*, 29(12), 1359–1372. DOI: 10.1016/ j.chiabu.2005.06.006

182. Edelson, M. G. (2010) Sexual abuse of children with autism: Factors that increase risk and interfere with recognition of abuse. *Disabilities Studies Quarterly*, 30(1).

Accessed online on 13/6/20 at https://dsq-sds.org/article/view/1058/1228

183. Pecora, L. A., Hancock, G. I., Mesibov, G. B. & Stokes, M. A. (2019) Characterising the sexuality and sexual experiences of autistic females. *Journal of Autism and Developmental Disorders*, 49(12), 4834–4846. DOI: 10.1007/s10803-019-04204-9

184. Ministry of Justice, Home Office & Office for National Statistics (2013) *An Overview of Sexual Offending in England and Wales.* Accessed online on 13/6/20 at https://webarchive.nationalarchives.gov.uk/20160106113426/www.ons.gov.uk/ons/rel/crime-stats/an-overview-of-sexual-offending-in-england---wales/december-2012/index.html

185. Ohlsson, G. V., Lichtenstein, P., Långström, N. & Pettersson, E. (2018) Childhood neurodevelopmental disorders and risk of coercive sexual victimization in childhood and adolescence: A population-based prospective twin study. *Journal of Child Psychology and Psychiatry*, 59(9), 957–965. DOI: 10.1111/jcpp.12884

186. Bargiela, S., Steward, R. & Mandy, W. (2016) The experiences of late-diagnosed women with autism spectrum conditions: An investigation of the female autism phenotype. *Journal of Autism and Developmental Disorders*, 46(10), 3281–3294. https://doi.org/10.1007/s10803-016-2872-8

187. Russell, C. (Director) (2017) *Chris Packham: Asperger's and me* [TV documentary]. BBC.

188. Smith DaWalt, L., Hong, J., Greenberg, J. S. & Mailick, M. R. (2019) Mortality in individuals with autism spectrum disorder: Predictors over a 20-year period. *Autism: The International Journal of Research and Practice*, 23(7), 1732–1739. https://doi.org/10.1177/1362361319827412

189. Bilder, D., Botts, E. L., Smith, K. R., Pimentel, R., Farley, M., Viskochil, J. et al. (2013) Excess mortality and causes of death in autism spectrum disorders: A follow up of the 1980s Utah/UCLA Autism Epidemiologic Study. *Journal of Autism and Developmental Disorders*, 43, 1196–1204. https://doi.org/10.1007/s10803-012-1664-z

190. Mouridsen, S. E., Brønnum-Hansen, H., Rich, B. & Isager, T. (2008) Mortality and causes of death in autism spectrum disorders: An update. *Autism*, 12(4), 403–414. DOI: 10.1177/1362361308091653

191. Duchan, E. & Patel, D. R. (2012) Epidemiology of autism spectrum disorders. *Pediatric Clinics of North America*, 59(1), 27–43. DOI: 10.1016/j.pcl.2011.10.003

192. Gillberg, C., Billstedt, E., Sundh, V. & Gillberg, I. C. (2010) Mortality in autism: A prospective longitudinal community-based study. *Journal of Autism and Developmental Disorders*, 40(3), 352–357. DOI: 10.1007/s10803-009-0883-4

193. Isager, T., Mouridsen, S. E. & Rich, B. (1999) Mortality and causes of death in pervasive developmental disorders. *Autism*, 3(1), 7–16. DOI: 10.1177/1362361399003001002

194. Shavelle, R. M. & Strauss, D. (1998) Comparative mortality of persons with autism in California, 1980–1996. *Journal of Insurance Medicine*, 30(4), 220–225. Accessed online on 14/6/20 at http://worl.lifeexpectancy.com/articles/a1.pdf

195. Cassidy, S., Bradley, P., Robinson, J., Allison, C., McHugh, M. & Baron-Cohen, S. (2014) Suicidal ideation and suicide plans or attempts in adults with Asperger's syndrome attending a specialist diagnostic clinic: A clinical cohort study. *The Lancet Psychiatry*, 1(2), 142–147.

196. South, M., Beck, J. S., Lundwall, R., Christensen, M., Cutrer, E. A., Gabrielsen, T. P. et al. (2019) Unrelenting depression and suicidality in women with autistic traits. *Journal of Autism and Developmental Disorders*. https://doi.org/10.1007/s10803-019-04324-2

197. Kirby, A. V., Bakian, A. V., Zhang, Y., Bilder, D. A., Keeshin, B. R. & Coon, H. (2019) A 20-year study of suicide death in a statewide autism population. *Autism Research*, 12, 658–666. DOI: 10.1002/aur.2076

198. Richards, G., Kenny, R., Griffiths, S., Allison, C., Mosse, D., Holt, R. et al. (2019) Autistic traits in adults who have attempted suicide. *Molecular Autism*, 10(26). DOI: 10.1186/s13229-019-0274-4

199. Hedley, D. & Uljarević, M. (2018) Systematic review of suicide in autism spectrum disorder: Current trends and implications. *Current Developmental Disorders Reports*, 5, 65–76. https://doi.org/10.1007/s40474-018-0133-6

200. Karakoç, D. S., Tutkunkardaş, M. D. & Mukaddes, N. M. (2016) Assessment of suicidality in children and adolescents with diagnosis of high functioning autism spectrum disorder in a Turkish clinical sample. *Neuropsychiatric Disease and Treatment*, 12, 2921–2926. DOI: 10.2147/NDT.S118304

201. Huguet, G., Contejean, Y. & Doyen, C. (2015) Troubles du spectre autistique et suicidalité [Autism spectrum disorder and suicidality]. *Encephale*, 41(4), 362–369. DOI: 10.1016/j.encep.2014.08.010

202. Gillberg, C. (2002) *A Guide to Asperger Syndrome*. Cambridge: Cambridge University Press. DOI: 10.1017/CBO9780511543814

203. Horowitz, L. M., Thurm, A., Farmer, C., Mazefsky, C., Lanzillo, E., Bridge, J. A. et al. (2017) Talking about death or suicide: Prevalence and clinical correlates in youth with autism spectrum disorder in the psychiatric inpatient setting. *Journal of Autism and Developmental Disorders.* https://doi.org/10.1007/s10803-017-3180-7

204. Cassidy, S., Bradley, L., Shaw, R. & Baron-Cohen, S. (2018) Risk markers for suicidality in autistic adults. *Molecular Autism*, 9, 42. https://doi.org/10.1186/s13229-018-0226-4

205. Cassidy, S. A., Gould, K., Townsend, E., Pelton, M., Robertson, A. E. & Rodgers, J. (2019) Is camouflaging autistic traits associated with suicidal thoughts and behaviours? Expanding the interpersonal psychological theory of suicide in an undergraduate student sample. *Journal of Autism and Developmental Disorders.* https://doi.org/10.1007/s10803-019-04323-3

206. Arwert, T. G. & Sizoo, B. B. (2020) Self-reported suicidality in male and female adults with autism spectrum disorders: Rumination and self-esteem. *Journal of Autism and Developmental Disorders.* https://doi.org/10.1007/s10803-020-04372-z

207. Howe, S. J., Hewitt, K., Baraskewich, J., Cassidy, S. & McMorris, C. A. (2020) Suicidality among children and youth with and without autism spectrum disorder: A systematic review of existing risk assessment tools. *Journal of Autism and Developmental Disorders*, 50, 3462–3476. https://doi.org/10.1007/s10803-020-04394-7

208. Coleman-Fountain, E., Buckley, C. & Beresford, B. (2020) Improving mental health in autistic young adults: A qualitative study exploring help-seeking barriers in UK primary care. *British Journal of General Practice*, 70(694), e356–e363. DOI: 10.3399/bjgp20X709421

209. Jager-Hyman, S., Maddox, B. B., Crabbe, S. R. & Mandell, D. S. (2020) Mental health clinicians' screening and intervention practices to reduce suicide risk in autistic adolescents and adults. *Journal of Autism and Developmental Disorders*, 50, 3450–3461. https://doi.org/10.1007/s10803-020-04441-3

210. Wightman, K. (Executive Producer) (2020) *Panorama* [TV series]: Failed by the NHS: Callie's story. BBC. Accessed online at www.bbc.co.uk/programmes/m000f9d2

211. Weiner, L., Flin, A., Causin, J., Weibel, S. & Bertschy, G. (2019) A case study of suicidality presenting as a restricted interest in autism spectrum disorder. *BMC Psychiatry*, 19, Article No. 126. https://doi.org/10.1186/s12888-019-2122-7

212. Vance, T. (2019) Why your Asperger's–NT relationship is failing. Psych Central. Accessed online on 9/7/20 at https://blogs.psychcentral.com/aspie/2019/04/why-your-aspergers-nt-relationship-is-failing/

213. Grandin, T. (1984) My experiences as an autistic child. *Journal of Orthomolecular Psychiatry*, 13(3), 144–174.

214. Sinclair, J. (1992) Bridging the gaps: An inside-out view of autism. In E. Schopler & G. B. Mesibov (eds), *High-Functioning Individuals with Autism* (pp. 294–302). New York: Plenum Press.

215. Blackburn, R. (2011) Logically illogical: The perspective of an adult with autism. In *Autism Residential Weekend, University of Birmingham, Birmingham, 23–25 September 2011*.

216. Gernsbacher, M. A., Morson, E. M. & Grace, E. J. (2016) Language development in autism. In G. Hickok & S. L. Small (eds), *Neurobiology of Language* (pp. 879–886). London: Academic Press.

217. Hudry, K., Leadbitter, K., Temple, K., Slonims, V., McConachie, H., Aldred, C. et al. (2010) Preschoolers with autism show greater impairment in receptive compared with expressive language abilities. *International Journal of Language and Communication Disorders*, 45(6), 681–690.

218. Boucher, J. (2012) Research review: Structural language in autistic spectrum disorder – characteristics and causes. *Journal of Child Psychology and Psychiatry, and Allied Disciplines*, 53(3), 219–233.

219. Weismer, S. E., Lord, C. & Esler, A. (2010) Early language patterns of toddlers on the autism spectrum compared to toddlers with developmental delay. *Journal of Autism and Developmental Disorders*, 40(10), 1259–1273.

220. Chan, A. S., Cheung, J., Leung, W. W., Cheung, R.& Cheung, M. C. (2005) Verbal expression and comprehension deficits in young children with autism. *Focus on Autism and Other Developmental Disabilities*, 20(2), 117–124.

221. Brignell, A., Williams, K., Jachno, K., Prior, M., Reilly, S. & Morgan, A. T. (2018) Patterns and predictors of language development from 4 to 7 years in verbal children with and without autism spectrum disorder. *Journal of Autism and Developmental Disorders*, 48(10), 3282–3295.

222. Sahyoun, C. P., Soulieres, I., Belliveau, J. W., Mottron, L. & Mody, M. (2009) Cognitive differences in pictorial reasoning between high-functioning autism and Asperger's syndrome. *Journal of Autism and Developmental Disorders*, 39(7), 1014–1023.

223. Vulchanova, M., Chahboun, S., Galindo-Prieto, B. & Vulchanov, V. (2019) Gaze and motor traces of language processing: Evidence from autism spectrum disorders in comparison to typical controls. *Cognitive Neuropsychology*, 36(7–8), 383–409.

224. Venker, C. E. (2017) Spoken word recognition in children with autism spectrum disorder: The role of visual disengagement. *Autism*, 21(7), 821–829.

225. Eigsti, I.-M., de Marchena, A. B., Schuh, J. M. & Kelley, E. (2011) Language acquisition in autism spectrum disorders: A developmental review. *Research in Autism Spectrum Disorders*, 5(2), 681–691.

226. American Psychiatric Association (1980) *Diagnostic and Statistical Manual of Mental Disorders* (3rd edition). Washington, DC: American Psychiatric Association.

227. American Psychiatric Association (2013) *Diagnostic and Statistical Manual of Mental Disorders* (5th edition). Arlington, VA: American Psychiatric Publishing.

228. Kossyvaki, L. (2013) Adult interactive style and autism: Reviewing the literature to inform school practice. *Good Autism Practice*, 14(2), 23–32.

229. Potter, C. & Whittaker, C. (2001) *Enabling Communication in Children with Autism*. London, UK: Jessica Kingsley Publishers.

230. Ingersoll, B. (2011) The differential effect of three naturalistic language interventions on language use in children with autism. *Journal of Positive Behavior Interventions*, 13(2), 109–118.

231. McAteer, M. & Wilkinson, M. (2009) Adult style: What helps to facilitate interaction and communication with children on the autism spectrum. *Good Autism Practice*, 10(2), 57–63.

232. Gillett, J. N. & LeBlanc, L. A. (2007) Parent-implemented natural language paradigm to increase language and play in children with autism. *Research in Autism Spectrum Disorders*, 1(3), 247–255.

233. Kossyvaki, L., Jones, G. & Guldberg, K. (2016) Training teaching staff to facilitate spontaneous communication in children with autism: Adult Interactive Style Intervention (AISI). *Journal of Research in Special Educational Needs*, 16(3), 156–168.

234. Kossyvaki, L., Jones, G. & Guldberg, K. (2012) The effect of Adult Interactive Style on the spontaneous communication of young children with autism at school. *British Journal of Special Education*, 39(4), 173–184.

235. Singer, J. (2016) *NeuroDiversity: The Birth of an Idea* (2nd edition). Lëtzebuerg, Luxembourg: Amazon Media EU.

236. Walker, N. (2020) The Neurodiversity Paradigm. Autistic UK CIC. Accessed on 12/6/20 at https://autisticuk.org/neurodiversity/

237. DuBois, D., Ameis, S. H., Lai, M-C., Casanova, M. F. & Desarkar, P. (2016) Interoception in autism spectrum disorder: A review. *International Journal of Developmental Neuroscience*, 52, 104–111.

238. Garfinkel, S. N., Tiley, C., O'Keeffe, S., Harrison, N. A., Seth, A. K. & Critchley, H. D. (2016) Discrepancies between dimensions of interoception in autism: Implications for emotion and anxiety. *Biological Psychology*, 114, 117–126.

239. Hatfield, T. R., Brown, R. F., Giummarra, M. J. & Lenggenhager, B. (2019) Autism spectrum disorder and interoception: Abnormalities in global integration? *Autism: The International Journal of Research and Practice*, 23(1), 212–222. https://doi.org/10.1177/1362361317738392

240. Mul, C., Stagg, S. D., Herbelin, B. & Aspell, J. E. (2018) The feeling of me feeling for you: Interoception, alexithymia and empathy in autism. *Journal of Autism and Developmental Disorders*, 48, 2953–2967. https://doi.org/10.1007/s10803-018-3564-3

241. Palser, E. R., Fotopoulou, A., Pellicano, E. & Kilner, J. M. (2020) Dissociation in how core autism features relate to interoceptive dimensions: Evidence from cardiac awareness in children. *Journal of Autism and Developmental Disorders*, 50, 572–582. https://doi.org/10.1007/s10803-019-04279-4

242. Quattrocki, E. & Friston, K. (2014) Autism, oxytocin and interoception. *Neuroscience & Biobehavioral Reviews*, 47, 410–430.

243. Seth, A. K. & Friston, K. J. (2016) Active interoceptive inference and the emotional brain. *Philosophical Transactions of the Royal Society B*, 37120160007.

244. Soker-Elimaliah, S., Jennings, C. A., Hashimi, M. M., Cassim, T. Z., Lehrfield, A. & Wagner, J. B. (2020) Autistic traits moderate relations between cardiac autonomic activity, interoceptive accuracy, and emotion processing in college students. *International Journal of Psychophysiology*, 155, 118–126.

245. Dijkhuis, R. R., Ziermans, T. B., Van Rijn, S., Staal, W. G., & Swaab, H. (2017) Self-regulation and quality of life in high-functioning young adults with autism. *Autism: The*

International Journal of Research and Practice, 21(7), 896–906. https://doi.org/10.1177/1362361316655525

246. De Groot, K. & Van Strien, J. W. (2017) Self-report and brain indicators of impaired emotion regulation in the broad autism spectrum. *Journal of Autism and Developmental Disorders*, 47(7), 2138–2152. https://doi.org/10.1007/s10803-017-3138-9

247. Richey, J. A., Damiano, C. R., Sabatino, A., Rittenberg, A., Petty, C., Bizzell, J. et al. (2015) Neural mechanisms of emotion regulation in autism spectrum disorder. *Journal of Autism and Developmental Disorders*, 45, 3409–3423.

248. Lartseva, A., Dijkstra, T. & Buitelaar, J. K. (2015) Emotional language processing in autism spectrum disorders: A systematic review. *Frontiers in Human Neuroscience*, 8, Article 991, 1–24. https://doi.org/10.3389/fnhum.2014.00991

249. Moseley, R. L., Shtyrov, Y., Mohr, B., Lombardo, M. V., Baron-Cohen, S. & Pulvermüller, F. (2015) Lost for emotion words: What motor and limbic brain activity reveals about autism and semantic theory. *NeuroImage*, 104, 413–422. https://doi.org/10.1016/j.neuroimage.2014.09.046

250. Mazefsky, C. A. (2015) Emotion regulation and emotional distress in autism spectrum disorder: Foundations and considerations for future research. *Journal of Autism and Developmental Disorders*, 45(11), 3405–3408. https://doi.org/10.1007/s10803-015-2602-7

251. Pitskel, N. B., Bolling, D. Z., Kaiser, M. D., Pelphrey, K. P. & Crowley, M. J. (2014) Neural systems for cognitive reappraisal in children and adolescents with autism spectrum disorder. *Developmental Cognitive Neuroscience*, 10, 117–128.

252. Mazefsky, C. A., Borue, X., Day, T. N. & Minshew, N. J. (2014) Emotion regulation patterns in adolescents with high-functioning autism spectrum disorder: Comparison to typically developing adolescents and association with psychiatric symptoms. *Autism Research*, 7, 344–354.

253. Jahromi, L. B., Meek, S. E. & Ober-Reynolds, S. (2012) Emotion regulation in the context of frustration in children with high functioning autism and their typical peers. *Journal of Child Psychology and Psychiatry, and Allied Disciplines*, 53(12), 1250–1258. https://doi.org/10.1111/j.1469-7610.2012.02560.x

254. Samson, A. C., Huber, O. & Gross, J. J. (2012) Emotion regulation in Asperger's syndrome and high-functioning autism. *Emotion*, 12, 659–665.

255. Glaser, S. & Shaw, S. (2011) Emotion regulation and development in children with autism and 22q13 Deletion Syndrome: Evidence for group differences. *Research in Autism Spectrum Disorders*, 5, 926–934. DOI: 10.1016/j.rasd.2010.11.001

256. Hill, E., Berthoz, S. & Frith, U. (2004) Brief report: Cognitive processing of own emotions in individuals with autistic spectrum disorder and in their relatives. *Journal of Autism and Developmental Disorders*, 34, 229–235. https://doi.org/10.1023/B:JADD.0000022613.41399.14

257. McDonnell, A. & Milton, D. (2014) Going with the flow: Reconsidering 'repetitive behaviour' through the concept of 'flow states'. In G. Jones & E. Hurley (eds), *Good Autism Practice: Autism, Happiness and Wellbeing* (pp. 38–47). Birmingham: British Institute of Learning Disabilities.

258. Gomez, C. R. & Baird, S. (2005) Identifying early indicators for autism in self-regulation difficulties. *Focus on Autism and Other Developmental Disabilities*, 20, 106–117.

259. Kinnaird, E., Stewart, C. & Tchanturia, K. (2019) Investigating alexithymia in autism: A systematic review and meta-analysis. *European Psychiatry*, 55, 80–89. DOI: 10.1016/j.eurpsy.2018.09.004

260. Poquérusse, J., Pastore, L., Dellantonio, S. & Esposito, G. (2018) Alexithymia and autism spectrum disorder: A complex relationship. *Frontiers in Psychology*, 9, 1196. Accessed online on 2/7/20 at www.frontiersin.org/articles/10.3389/fpsyg.2018.01196/full

261. Bird, G., Press, C. & Richardson, D. C. (2011) The role of alexithymia in reduced eye-fixation in autism spectrum conditions. *Journal of Autism and Developmental Disorders*, 41, 556–1564. DOI: 10.1007/s10803-011-1183-3

262. Bird, G., Silani, G., Brindley, R., White, S., Frith, U. & Singer, T. (2010) Empathic brain responses in insula modulated by levels of alexithymia but not autism. *Brain*, 133, 1515–1525. DOI: 10.1093/brain/awq060

263. Silani, G., Bird, G., Brindley, R., Singer, T., Frith, C. & Frith, U. (2008) Levels of emotional awareness and autism: An fMRI study. *Social Neuroscience*, 3, 97–112. DOI: 10.1080/17470910701577020

264. Lombardo, M. V., Barnes, J. L., Wheelwright, S. J., & Baron-Cohen, S. (2007) Self-referential cognition and empathy in autism. *PLoS ONE*, 2(9), e883. DOI: 10. 1371/journal.pone.0000883

265. Linden, W.,Wen, F., & Paulhus, D. L. (1995) Measuring alexithymia: Reliability, validity and prevalence. In J. Butcher & C. Spielberger (eds), *Advances in Personality Assessment*, (pp. 51–95). Hillsdale, NJ: Earlbaum.

266. Salminen, J. K., Saarijärvi, S., Äärelä, E., Toikka, T. & Kauhanen, J. (1999) Prevalence of alexithymia and its association with socio demographic variables in the general population of Finland. *Journal of Psychosomatic Research*, 46, 75–82. DOI: 10. 1016/s0022-3999(98)00053-1

267. Dark, J. (2019) The beauty and the darkness of stimming, supporting sensory regulation. Hygge Me. [Blog no longer available online]

268. BBC UX&D Staff (2019) Meet Jamie + Lion, Senior Research Engineer. BBC. Accessed online on 25/6/20 at www.bbc.co.uk/gel/articles/meet-jamie-knight

269. Rose, B. (2016) Jamie and his Lion: The adults who take their soft toys to work. BBC. Accessed online on 25/6/20 at www.bbc.co.uk/news/disability-37560841

270. Burgess, M. (Producer) (2017) Jo and Andy – Divorce. BBC Radio 4, The Listening Project, January 1. Accessed online on 25/6/20 at www.bbc.co.uk/sounds/play/b086l8m4

271. Grace, H. & Grace, J. (2020) *My Mummy Is Autistic: A Picture Book and Guide about Recognising and Understanding Difference*. Abingdon: Routledge.

272. Dworzynski, K., Ronald, A., Bolton, P. & Happé, F. (2012) How different are girls and boys above and below the diagnostic threshold for autism spectrum disorders? *Journal of the American Academy of Child and Adolescent Psychiatry*, 51(8), 788–797.

273. Women and Work All-Part Parliamentary Group (2020) *Inclusivity and Intersectionality: Toolkit and Annual Report 2019*. London, UK: Connect. Accessed online on 26/6/20 at: https://connectpa.co.uk/wp-content/uploads/2020/02/Women-and-work-Annual-report-2019-A4.pdf

274. Baldwin, S. & Costley, D. (2015) The experiences and needs of female adults with high-functioning autism spectrum disorder. *Autism: The International Journal of Research and Practice*, 20(4), 483–495. https://doi.org/10.1177/1362361315590805

275. Cheslack-Postava, K. & Jordan-Young, R. M. (2012) Autism spectrum disorders. *Social Science and Medicine*, 74, 1667–1674.

276. Hull, L., Petrides, K. V. & Mandy, W. (2020) The female autism phenotype and camouflaging: A narrative review.

Review Journal of Autism and Developmental Disorders. https://doi.org/10.1007/s40489-020-00197-9

277. Hudson, R. L. (2013) *The Effect of Disability Disclosure on the Graduation Rates of College Students with Disabilities* (Unpublished doctoral dissertation, Virginia Tech, VA). Accessed online on 27/6/20 at https://vtechworks.lib. vt.edu/handle/10919/24072

278. Fulton, A. M., Paynter, J. M. & Trembath, D. (2017) Gender comparisons in children with ASD entering early intervention. *Research in Developmental Disabilities*, 68, 27–34. https://doi.org/10.1016/j.ridd.2017.07.009

279. Beck, J. S., Lundwall, R. A., Gabrielsen, T., Cox, J. C. & South, M. (2020) Looking good but feeling bad: "Camouflaging" behaviors and mental health in women with autistic traits. *Autism*, 24(4), 809–821. https://doi.org/10.1177/1362361320912147

280. Hull, L., Lai, M. C., Baron-Cohen, S., Allison, C., Smith, P., Petrides, K. V. et al. (2019) Gender differences in self-reported camouflaging in autistic and non-autistic adults. *Autism*, 18, 1362361319864804.

281. Allely, C. S. (2019) Understanding and recognising the female phenotype of autism spectrum disorder and the "camouflage" hypothesis: A systematic PRISMA review. *Advances in Autism*, 5(1), 14–37. https://doi.org/10.1108/AIA-09-2018-0036

282. Cook, A., Ogden, J. & Winstone, N. (2018) Friendship motivations, challenges and the role of masking for girls with autism in contrasting school settings. *European Journal of Special Needs Education*, 33(3), 302–315. DOI: 10.1080/08856257.2017.1312797

283. Lai, M. C., Lombardo, M. V., Ruigrok, A. N., Chakrabarti, B., Auyeung, B., Szatmari, P. et al.(2017) Quantifying and exploring camouflaging in men and women with autism. *Autism: The International Journal of Research and Practice*, 21(6), 690–702. https://doi.org/10.1177/1362361316671012

284. Rynkiewicz, A., Schuller, B., Marchi, E., Piana, S., Camurri, A., Lassalle, A. et al. (2016) An investigation of the 'female camouflage effect' in autism using a computerized ADOS-2 and a test of sex/gender differences. *Molecular Autism*, 7, 10. https://doi.org/10.1186/s13229-016-0073-0

285. Hull, L., Petrides, K. V., Allison, C., Smith, P., Baron-Cohen, S., Lai, M. C. et al. (2017) "Putting on my best normal": Social camouflaging in adults with autism spectrum conditions.

Journal of Autism and Developmental Disorders, 47(8), 2519–2534. https://doi.org/10.1007/s10803-017-3166-5

286. Livingston, L. A., Colvert, E., Social Relationships Study Team, Bolton, P. & Happé, F. (2019) Good social skills despite poor theory of mind: Exploring compensation in autism spectrum disorder. *Journal of Child Psychology and Psychiatry, and Allied Disciplines*, 60(1), 102–110. https://doi.org/10.1111/jcpp.12886

287. Mandy, W. (2019) Social camouflaging in autism: Is it time to lose the mask? *Autism*, 23(8), 1879–1881. https://doi.org/10.1177/1362361319878559

288. Cage, E., Di Monaco, J. & Newell, V. (2018) Experiences of Autism Acceptance and mental health in autistic adults. *Journal of Autism and Developmental Disorders*, 48, 473–484. https://doi.org/10.1007/s10803-017-3342-7

289. Somerville, M., MacPherson, S. E. & Fletcher-Watson, S. (2019, November 24) Camouflaging in non-autistic adults is associated with poorer mental health. PsyArxiv preprints. https://doi.org/10.31234/osf.io/myp4g

290. Cage, E. & Troxell-Whitman, Z. (2019) Understanding the reasons, contexts and costs of camouflaging for autistic adults. *Journal of Autism and Developmental Disorders*, 49, 1899–1911. https://doi.org/10.1007/s10803-018-03878-x

291. Tierney, S., Burns, J. & Kilbey, E. (2016) Looking behind the mask: Social coping strategies of girls on the autistic spectrum. *Research in Autism Spectrum Disorders*, 23, 73–83.

292. Oxford Reference (2014) Autism. Online Oxford Reference Dictionary. Accessed on 2/7/20 at www.oxfordreference.com/view/10.1093/acref/9780199212064.001.0001/acref-9780199212064-e-83

Notes

Chapter 11 Reflecting on the impact of diagnosis on my identity

1 This book was written during the UK's 2020 first lockdown period as the country responded to the global COVID-19 pandemic.
2 You will see too as you finish the book.
3 The Autistic Self Advocacy Network (2020) compiled a list of more than 1300 reported murders of people with disabilities by relatives or caregivers over the last 39 years. The actual number of murders is likely to be higher as not every murder will be reported in the news media.

Chapter 16 Love across a neurodiverse divide (explanations of a photoblog)

1 The Three Mountains Experiment was developed by Jean Piaget to discern the level of a child's cognitive development, ascertaining whether they perceived the world in an egocentric way or could imagine themselves in another's position and understand their perspective.
2 The Police Doll Experiment was developed by Martin Hughes; it achieves the same as the Three Mountains Experiment. Hughes thought the use of a police doll might be easier for children to understand and more motivating in that the narrative of the policeman looking for someone gives a reason to try to understand the perspective of the police doll.

3 The Sally Anne Test was developed by Simon Baron-Cohen, Alan Leslie and Uta Frith, the nature of the test is described in section 10.6. Once again it is looking to ascertain whether the person doing the test can imagine the perspective of another person.

Chapter 18   Emotional connection

1 Jamie and Lion work for the BBC: they are active on Twitter at: @Spacedoutmiles, @JamieKnight and @Lickr and blog at http://spacedoutandsmiling.com

Index

Printed in Great Britain
by Amazon

66366812R00183